ALEKS™
Instructor's Manual

Harold D. Baker, Ph.D.

ALEKS Corporation

Boston   Burr Ridge, IL   Dubuque, IA   Madison, WI   New York   San Francisco   St. Louis
Bangkok   Bogotá   Caracas   Lisbon   London   Madrid
Mexico City   Milan   New Delhi   Seoul   Singapore   Sydney   Taipei   Toronto

McGraw-Hill Higher Education

*A Division of The **McGraw-Hill** Companies*

ALEKS INSTRUCTOR'S MANUAL

ALEKS is a trademark of ALEKS Corporation in the United States and other countries.

 This book is printed on recycled paper containing 10% postconsumer waste.
RECYCLED

1 2 3 4 5 6 7 8 9 0 QPD QPD 9 0 3 2 1 0 9

ISBN 0-07-239908-2

www.mhhe.com

Contents

List of Figures

Preface

Congratulations on your interest in **ALEKS**! This is an online educational system like none you have encountered before, whose use of computer technology to promote math learning is pedagogically sound and cutting-edge.

The **features** of **ALEKS** make it a self-contained tool, opening new horizons for educators and learners alike in any educational context. The **ALEKS** Course Management System enables college math instructors to oversee and monitor their students' progress, communicate with them, track usage levels, and focus instruction. By its unprecedented use of Artificial Intelligence, **ALEKS** determines quickly and precisely what your students know and what they need to learn, guiding them down individualized learning paths to mastery. Assessment and practice problems are algorithmically generated, so the students cannot predict them. The syllabi used in **ALEKS** are customizable, letting you add or subtract topics from your course with a click of the mouse. Since it is accessed over the World Wide Web using standard browsers, no complicated technical preparation is needed—and your students can work on their accounts at any time, from home or from the lab! **ALEKS** is fully integrated with McGraw-Hill math textbooks and a variety of other online learning resources. And the price is low: no setup fees, no site licenses. It's a personal tutor for each of your students, at a fraction of what such services normally cost.

The **benefits** of using **ALEKS** are striking. Students work in a dynamic, interactive learning environment on precisely those materials that they are individually ready to learn, building momentum toward mastery. Students love **ALEKS**, because *they* call the shots, working on their own schedule on what they need to learn right now. It is the personalized "just-in-time" learning system.

ALEKS may be used in a variety of developmental math courses—whether in a traditional classroom, or in a self-directed or distance-learning environment. **ALEKS** is sold to the student as a subscription. The student purchases a *User's Guide* with Access Code, usually through the bookstore. Using this Access Code along with the Course Code provided by the instructor, the student registers in the **ALEKS** system at the **ALEKS** Higher Education website. Your sales representative will provide you with a Course Code once your order for *User's Guide*s has been submitted to McGraw-Hill by your bookstore.

ALEKS can be adopted in one of three ways:

- **ALEKS** may be adopted as a supplement to a McGraw-Hill textbook. When you adopt **ALEKS** as a supplement, the student subscription cost is similar to the cost of a traditional print supplement, such as a student solutions manual. There is a special version of **ALEKS** to accompany most of McGraw-Hill's developmental math textbooks. This version allows the student to see references within **ALEKS** to the textbooks and provides links to the McGraw-Hill book-specific websites. These websites include additional tutorial material and interactive applications that supplement the explanations within **ALEKS**. If you adopt **ALEKS** as a supplement, students will need to purchase a McGraw-Hill textbook bundled with the *User's Guide* with Access Code.

- **ALEKS** may be adopted as a stand-alone item. In this case, the instructor adopts **ALEKS** alone and the students purchase the *User's Guide* with Access Code for about the cost of a traditional textbook.

- **ALEKS** may be adopted with any of the course-specific **ALEKS** Worktexts. Each Worktext provides additional worked examples and practice problems for the student to use when a computer is not available. The Worktext websites provide additional tutorial material and interactive applications. Electronic files of the Worktexts available by section online; this way students can hand in the printed Worktext pages as homework and still have access to the additional worked examples for reference.

This *Instructor's Manual* is intended to provide complete information on the functioning of the **ALEKS** system. A description of its contents can be found in the Introduction (Chap. 1).

ALEKS: An Instructor's Video, packaged with this *Instructor's Manual*, prepares you to use **ALEKS**. In the video, you will meet the cognitive scientist, Jean-Claude Falmagne, who co-developed Knowledge Space theory and tapped its potential for developmental math instruction. To help you understand how **ALEKS** works—from both the student's and instructor's perspectives—you will see a thorough demonstration of its Assessment, Learning, and Instructor modules. Finally, you will hear math instructors discuss how **ALEKS** may be used in developmental math—whether in a traditional classroom or in a self-directed or distance-learning environment. The video is approximately 60 minutes in length. It is recommended that any instructor who will be assisting or instructing students using **ALEKS** take the time to watch the video.

Chapter 1

Introduction

1.1 What is ALEKS?

ALEKS is an online system for the assessment and individualized teaching of mathematics. It is accessed over the World Wide Web on any suitable computer, and is designed to allow the monitoring and management of entire courses and institutions. The core of the system is an efficient, adaptive assessment engine which determines quickly and precisely what an individual student knows. Based on that assessment data the system is able to offer material that the student is best able to learn at a given time. The **ALEKS** Learning Mode includes explanations and algorithmically generated practice problems, ongoing assessment of student knowledge, an online math dictionary, and facilities for review and collaborative help. It can be used on an independent basis or as a supplement to classroom instruction.

The **ALEKS** system is the product of years of cutting-edge research into the mathematical modeling of human knowledge (Chap. 8). The creators of **ALEKS** are cognitive scientists, software engineers, and university professors in the mathematical disciplines. In designing **ALEKS**, their goals were to achieve the utmost simplicity of use without compromising the depth, rigor, or richness of mathematics instruction at its inspirational best. **ALEKS** is a tool to empower both instructors and learners of math: it opens doors and windows into the assessment and representation of knowledge, and it breaks down barriers to success by recognizing the vast diversity of paths that lead to mastery. The **ALEKS** system can make a radical difference in how math learning is experienced.

1.2 The ALEKS Instructor's Manual

The purpose of the **ALEKS** *Instructor's Manual* is to give instructors using **ALEKS** information on the operation of the system that is as complete as possible. The system is not complex. **ALEKS** can be and often is used with no documentation whatsoever. At the same time, we wish to offer instructors a clear idea of everything **ALEKS** does, how it works, and where to find answers to their students' questions.

ALEKS is designed to be used without help from a manual. Feel free to use your Access Code to register and use the system now. If questions arise, or if you want to learn more about ALEKS, this manual is intended as a convenient and comprehensive reference.

- Chapter 2, "Setup Guide for Instructors," provides all information necessary for preparing to use **ALEKS** with one or more courses. This ranges from technical requirements and installation through the students' first **ALEKS** session (which typically involves registration, tutorial, initial assessment, and entry into the Learning Mode). Much of the information is the same as that in Appendix A, but it is given from an instructor's viewpoint.

- Chapters 3 through 6 contain descriptions of the principal parts of the **ALEKS** system: Assessment Module, Learning Module, and Instructor Module. The Instructor Module is treated in two chapters. One covers Results & Progress, the facility for monitoring student use of **ALEKS** and managing accounts. The second covers Standards & Syllabi, the facility for reviewing and modifying the curricular information used by **ALEKS** for a particular college or course.

- Chapters 7 through 10 provide additional information which may be necessary or of interest to instructors using **ALEKS**. Chapter 7 contains suggestions on the most effective educational use of **ALEKS**, including ways to integrate it with overall course structure. Chapter 8, "Knowledge Spaces," explains the history of Knowledge Space theory and its fundamental concepts, along with the evolution of **ALEKS** itself. There is a Bibliography for those seeking to understand the theory behind **ALEKS** in greater depth. Chapter 9 provides answers to frequently asked questions about **ALEKS**. Chapter 10 gives the information necessary for obtaining technical and other support.
  NOTE: Instructors who need technical or other support in the use of ALEKS should turn to the form at the end of Chapter 10 (Sec. 10.2).

- The **ALEKS** *User's Guide* is distributed to all students using **ALEKS** in college mathematics courses. The *User's Guide* is reproduced here in Appendix A. Unlike the other chapters of the **ALEKS** *Instructor's Manual*, Appendix A is addressed to student users of the system. It covers technical requirements, installation, registration, the Tutorial, and ordinary use of the system, as well as guidelines for effective use and troubleshooting tips. Appendix A can be used by instructors to obtain a brief but complete picture of how the system is used.

Chapter 2

Setup Guide for Instructors

2.1 Instructor Preparation

It is important that instructors using **ALEKS** with their classes clearly understand the system's functioning and the ideas that underlie it. Time should be taken to study all materials provided, including this manual and the **ALEKS** video, and to try out the system thoroughly. The supervisor for **ALEKS** use can contact ALEKS Corporation for consultation at any time, and preferably well in advance of the first session (Sec. 10.1).

2.2 Technical Requirements

The following table presents the technical requirements for **ALEKS** in summary form:

	PC	Macintosh
Operating System	Windows 95/98/NT4.0 or higher	MacOS 7.6.1 or higher
Processor	Pentium 133+ MHz (166+ preferred), Pentium II/III	
RAM Memory	32+ MB	32+ MB
Browser	Netscape 4.5 or higher, Explorer 4.0 or higher	Netscape 4.5 or higher
Modem Speed	28+ kbps	28+ kbps

Figure 2.1: Technical Requirements

Note that any of the kinds of direct connection (cable, ISDN, DSL) that are typical in computer labs are adequate for use with **ALEKS**. If your computer lab has security safeguards in place, you will need the cooperation of your LAN administrator, system administrator, or lab technician to install the **ALEKS** plugin.

NOTE: Netscape Communicator 4.0x (4.01, 4.02, etc.) is not compatible with **ALEKS** and should be upgraded to 4.5 or higher. This can be done from the Netscape website:

> **http://www.netscape.com**

A student using America Online 3.0 will have to upgrade to America Online 4.0 or higher to use **ALEKS**. This can be done from AOL.

2.3   Installation

Installation of the **ALEKS** plugin takes place from the **ALEKS** website for Higher Education:

> **http://www.highed.aleks.com**

NOTE: You must use this URL to access **ALEKS**. Although there are other **ALEKS** websites you may find using an Internet search engine, only this one contains your registration data as a licensed **ALEKS** instructor. It is advisable to mark this website in your browser with a "Bookmark" or "Favorite" or by creating a shortcut of some kind.

Close all applications other than your web browser before beginning installation.

Installation of the **ALEKS** plugin is automatic. If you attempt to use the system directly by clicking on "Be our Guest" or on "Register with ALEKS" it will automatically check to see whether your computer has the most recent plugin currently installed (Fig. 2.2). If it does not, it will download the plugin and ask for your permission to install. (This is not a high-risk operation for your computer.) When you grant permission, it will install. Following installation you must close and reopen your browser application. Installation is automatic for registered users as well.

If you need to download and install the plugin when this does not occur automatically, click on "Download the ALEKS plugin."

2.4   Registering as an Instructor

Before You Begin: In order to register as an **ALEKS** instructor you need your Instructor Access Code. Contact your McGraw-Hill sales representative to receive your Instructor Access Code. When you register with the **ALEKS** system your name is put into the database as an instructor and you are able to access the Instructor Module (Chaps. 5–6).

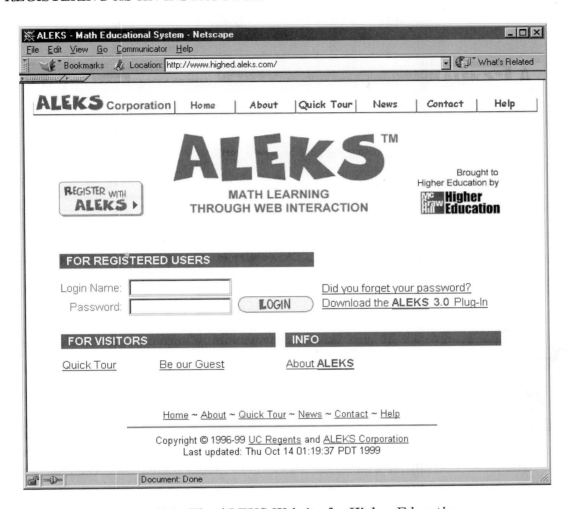

Figure 2.2: The ALEKS Website for Higher Education

Step 1: Go to the **ALEKS** website for Higher Education (use your Bookmark/Favorite, if you made one; Sec. 2.3):

   http://www.highed.aleks.com

Step 2: Click on "Register with ALEKS" (Fig. 2.2).

Step 3: You will see instructions for instructors registering with **ALEKS**. Click on "Register."

NOTE: If you do not have a current plugin the download and installation process will begin here (Sec. 2.3). When it is finished you will need to quit your Web browser ("Exit," "Close," or "Quit" under the "File" menu), open your Web browser again, and go back to the **ALEKS** website for Higher Education (use your Bookmark/Favorite for the **ALEKS** website). Return to Step 1, above, to begin

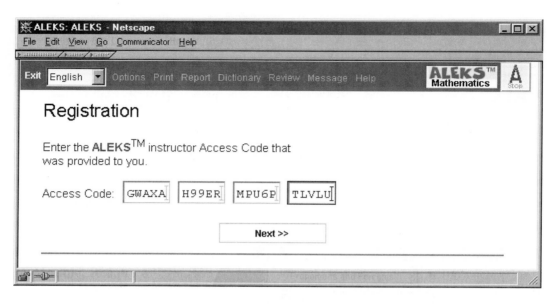

Figure 2.3: Access Code (for Instructor)

registration.

Step 4: At the beginning of registration you will be asked for your Instructor Access Code (available from your McGraw-Hill sales representative). Enter this in the spaces provided and click on "Next" (Fig. 2.3). Answer the questions to complete your registration. Among other questions, you will be asked to provide complete information on the course you are teaching with **ALEKS**. Following your registration as an instructor you will be able to use the Instructor Module to create additional classes if needed (Sec. 5.14).

Step 5: At the end of registration you will be given a Login Name and Password. Write these down and keep them in a safe place, since you will need them to return to the system. Your Login Name is not the same as your name, but usually consists of the first letter of your first name plus your last name in its entirety, with no spaces or punctuation. Thus "Jane Smith" may have the Login Name "jsmith"; if there is more than one "Jane Smith" in the database, a numeral will be appended, as "jsmith2." You can change your Password at any time.

NOTE: Login Name and Password can be typed with upper- or lower-case letters. Neither may contain spaces or punctuation.

Step 6: Following Registration you are also given the Course Code for the course you are teaching. Record and file this information carefully. This code must be supplied to your students when they first log on and register with **ALEKS** (Sec. 2.7).

2.5 Lab Check

To ensure the best possible experience of **ALEKS** for your students, we recommend that instructors check the computer lab in which **ALEKS** will be used in advance of the first session. This means installing and testing the plugin on some or (preferably) all of the computers in the lab. If security measures are in effect, you will need the cooperation of the lab administrator to install the plugin. To install and test, simply log on as guest to each computer (or use your instructor login). Installation will occur automatically. Following installation, restart the browsers and attempt login again. This time you should access **ALEKS**.

If the **ALEKS** plugin is not preinstalled and tested in this way, it will be installed when your students first access the system. This will take away a certain amount of time from their use of the system. Also, if there is some problem in the lab that makes installation difficult, it is far better to catch and resolve it before the students arrive.

2.6 Student Orientation

It is strongly recommended that the first **ALEKS** session be conducted under supervision, with one or more instructors on hand to help the students get started. Instructors may also choose to schedule supervised assessments at midterm and at the end of the course. It is not generally necessary to schedule a separate orientation meeting before the students actually begin using the system, although in some cases there may be reasons for doing so. Presumably, the students will all have copies of the **ALEKS** *User's Guide*. The instructor should encourage students to familiarize themselves with this brief guide. You may wish to remind them to bring it along to the first session as it contains their Access Code, which is required for registration. It is also advisable to emphasize the few requirements for assessments in **ALEKS**: paper and pencil are needed, simple calculators without graphic or symbolic functions are permitted for Algebra only, and no help whatsoever can be received by students being assessed. (A basic calculator is part of **ALEKS**.) Remind them that help is not allowed during the assessment because if the student being assessed does not do their own work, the assessment results may not be accurate, and this will hinder that student's progress in the Learning Mode.

If at all possible, the students' first session with **ALEKS** should be long enough for them to complete their assessments and begin work in the Learning Mode. One hour may be considered a minimum. Two hours is better, especially if more than one subject is being covered.

2.7   Registration

Students register with **ALEKS** by going to the **ALEKS** website for Higher Education and clicking on "Register with ALEKS." This will be expedited if the browsers used by the students have Bookmarks or Favorites pointing to the website (Sec. 2.3).

NOTE: In order to register, all students must have both their Access Code and the Course Code for the course that you are teaching. The students find the Access Code in their copy of the **ALEKS** *User's Guide,* inside the back cover. The Course Code is obtained by the instructor at the time of registration (Sec. 2.4). You are responsible for giving this code to the students at the time of the first session.

The student registration process is described in detail in the *User's Guide* (App. A). There are complete online instructions for every step of this simple procedure. Among other information, students are asked to supply their email address (so they can be helped more promptly in case of difficulties) and their Student ID number. Special care should be taken in entering the latter, as the system cannot detect mistyping.

Near the conclusion of Registration students receive a Login Name and Password. These should be noted carefully, as they will be essential for all further work with **ALEKS**. You may wish to advise the students to change their Passwords at the earliest opportunity. They should use a Password they will remember easily, but will be hard for others to guess. Login Name and Password can be typed with upper- or lower-case letters. Neither may contain spaces or punctuation.

2.8   Tutorial

Following Registration the students enter a brief tutorial on use of the **ALEKS** input tool, also called the "Answer Editor" (Sec. 3.5). There are separate Tutorials for different subjects since the specific tools for them differ somewhat. If the course covers more than one subject, all necessary Tutorials will be taken. The **ALEKS** Tutorial provides ample feedback to ensure that students complete it successfully.

NOTE: The Tutorial is not intended to teach mathematical knowledge, but rather to train students to use the system tools and to avoid multiple-choice problems. The correct input is always shown, and students simply enter what they see. If students need a "refresher" on use of the system tools, it is always possible to click on the "Help" button and review the instructions given there (Sec. 4.2.8).

2.9   First Assessment

Students proceed directly from the Tutorial to their first assessment (Chap. 3). To reiterate, no help of any kind should be given to students being assessed, not even to the extent of rephrasing a problem. Students need to have paper and pencil. Simple calculators (without graphic or symbolic functions) may be used for Algebra. (A basic calculator is part of **ALEKS**.) No calculators are used for Basic Math.

In courses combining more than one subject there will be an assessment for each domain. The **ALEKS** assessment is adaptive and variable in length. Some students will have very short assessments, whereas others will have assessments that are considerably longer. Consistency of effort and concentration is the factor most likely to influence the length of an assessment.

At the beginning of the assessment the students will be asked to estimate the approximate level of their knowledge in the subject. This information may make their assessments shorter, but has absolutely no effect on the assessment outcome. Students who don't know what level to indicate should select "Unknown."

2.10   Report Tutorial

At the conclusion of each assessment the student is given a brief Tutorial on how to interpret the Assessment Report. This will be in the form of one or more color-coded piecharts, with accompanying textual information (Sec. 3.6). It is extremely important that the students know how to interpret these piecharts correctly. Some instructors have found it worth the effort to sit with each student individually as they conclude their assessments. They can then make sure the students understand the parts of the Report and help them choose topics for entry into the Learning Mode.

Explain to students that subsequent assessments will produce only the piecharts. The piecharts also appear in the Learning Mode each time a new concept is mastered and "added to the pie" (or, conversely, not mastered). Pies can also be accessed by means of the "MyPie" button if the student wishes to choose a new topic.

2.11   Beginning the Learning Mode

Students enter the Learning Mode by clicking on one of the topics contained in their piechart (topics they are completely "ready to learn"). If at all possible, the students should be given sufficient time in their first **ALEKS** session to use the Learning Mode and, ideally, begin to "add concepts to their pie." If they have this experience, their interest in using **ALEKS** is likely to be more keen. The instructor is also present to answer questions regarding the Learning Mode and to assist the students in familiarizing themselves with its varied features. This is particularly important in cases where their subsequent use of **ALEKS** will be unsupervised.

Chapter 3

Assessment Module

The Assessment Module is the heart of the **ALEKS** system. Its ability to quickly and accurately determine a student's knowledge enables **ALEKS** to continuously make available the material the student can most readily employ, and thus efficiently guide individual learning paths. The Assessment and Learning Modules work together closely. In **ALEKS**, learning is powered and optimized by assessment.

3.1   Assessments in ALEKS

The **ALEKS** assessment uses open-ended problems (no multiple-choice). It is an adaptive assessment; that is, problem types are selected based on all the previous answers the student has given. It is impossible to predict which types of problems will appear, or in what order. Moreover, the problems themselves are generated algorithmically, with randomly selected numerical values (as is also the case in the Learning Mode). Thus, one cannot "learn the assessment" or "teach to the assessment," and surreptitious cheating is almost impossible. In the unlikely event that two students sitting next to one another were given the same problem-type at the same time, the numerical values would almost certainly be different, and so would the correct answer. Despite this, certain assessments must be supervised, such as the initial, midterm, and final assessments in a course. Without supervision, students could use a textbook, receive systematic help, or have someone else take the assessment in their place. This point is critical where assessment results are used for purposes other than those internal to the system. (There is no reason for a student who has begun using **ALEKS** to cheat on a "progress" assessment, as this will simply cause the system to suggest problems that are too difficult, and thus hinder the student's own work.)

As noted, the student takes an initial assessment immediately following completion of the Tutorial (Sec. 2.9). When an assessment begins, the student is clearly in-

11

formed it has begun, and, if it is an initial assessment, may be asked to choose an approximate skill level for the subject being assessed. This information is used only to attempt to make the assessment shorter. It has no effect whatsoever on the outcome or on the level at which the student will use **ALEKS**. (The student can always select "Unknown.") Next a series of mathematical problems is posed to the student. The student provides the solution to each problem using the Answer Editor (or clicks "I don't know"). In the Assessment Mode, the system does not inform the student whether the answer just given was correct or not. The assessment continues until the system has determined the student's precise knowledge of the domain, at which time the assessment ends and a report is presented to the student. The number of questions asked cannot be known in advance, although consistency of effort and attention seem to contribute to shorter assessments.

3.2   Rules for Assessments

Assessment in **ALEKS** is an important and serious event. It is essential that assessments be conducted according to certain guidelines and in the proper spirit. If there is an atmosphere permitting disturbances or distractions, the students will not obtain the benefits the system is capable of providing. If assessment results are inaccurate, the system will give the student inappropriate problems and progress will initially be impaired. The system will recover and find the right level, but the student may still experience a degree of frustration. In order to avoid this, it is strongly recommended that the first assessment be taken under the instructor's supervision (Sec. 2.9).

All students being assessed need paper and pencil. No calculators are permitted in assessments for Basic Math, but simple calculators (without symbolic or graphing functions) should be available for students being assessed in Algebra. A basic calculator is part of **ALEKS**. Most important, no assistance may be given—not even to the extent of explaining or rephrasing a problem. Students should be encouraged to use the "I don't know" button when they do not know what to do.

3.3   Scheduling of Assessments

The initial assessment takes place at the outset of students' use of **ALEKS**, immediately after Registration and Tutorial (Sec. 2.9). We strongly recommend that this initial assessment, which has the character of an orientation to the system for student users, take place in a supervised computer lab setting to ensure that students do not receive help or collaborate. In creating or editing a class account, the instructor can stipulate that the initial assessment be allowed only from school (Sec. 5.14). Additional assessments are scheduled automatically by the system based on two factors: overall time spent in the Learning Mode and progress made while

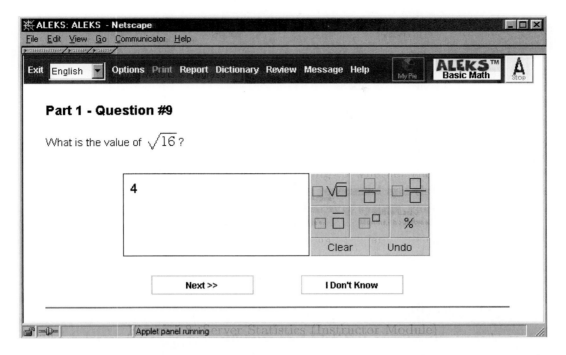

Figure 3.1: The Answer Editor for Mathematical Expressions (Assessment Mode)

there. The Learning Mode itself updates students' assessment results as it goes along, periodically displaying new piecharts and new choices of concepts they are completely "ready to learn." The automatic assessments, however, provide a firmer basis for such guidance.

Assessments can also be requested by the instructor for individual students or for entire courses. For example, the instructor may wish to have "midterm" assessments under supervision to guarantee sound results (or this may be a point of departmental policy). The instructor simply announces the assessment for a certain time and place. Just prior to this time the instructor prompts the course assessment in the Instructor Module (Secs. 5.7–5.8). The next time students log on they will automatically enter the assessment.

3.4   Menus

The Assessment Module (Fig. 3.1) has a reduced set of active menu buttons enabling the student being assessed to leave the system ("Exit") or get help on use of the Answer Editor ("Help"). Other buttons appear, but they are disabled. All of the **ALEKS** menu buttons are enabled in the Learning Mode.

The two aspects of the **ALEKS** interface relevant to work in the Assessment Mode

Expression	Answer Editor keypad button	Keyboard equivalent
Square Root	[ ]√[ ]	(none)
Fraction	⊢	/
Mixed Number	[ ]⊟	(none)
Repeating Decimal	[ ][ ]	(none)
Absolute Value	[ ] ‖[ ]‖	(none)
List of Expressions	[ ], [ ], …	,
Exponent	[ ]^[ ]	∧ (before exponent)
Multiplication Expression	[ ] × [ ]	*
Percentage	%	%
Greater-Than	[ ] > [ ]	>
Less-Than	[ ] < [ ]	<
Greater-Than-Or-Equal-To	[ ] ≥ [ ]	(none)
Less-Than-Or-Equal-To	[ ] ≤ [ ]	(none)
Equal-To	[ ] = [ ]	=
Not-Equal-To	[ ] ≠ [ ]	(none)
AND	*AND*	(none)
OR	*OR*	(none)

Figure 3.2: Mathematical Expressions Produced by the Answer Editor

are the Answer Editor and the Assessment Report.

3.5   Answer Editor

Input to the **ALEKS** system is always in the form of proper mathematical expressions and constructions, never multiple-choice. A critical reason for this is to prevent substantial inaccuracies which arise from students' guessing and trying out the different choices. Another purpose of this approach is to train students in the same skills that are necessary for conventional, paper-and-pencil communication of solutions and results. At the same time, the sophistication of the **ALEKS** input tools provides certain advantages. The presentation of results is always neat and clear. Manual dexterity plays a reduced role in, say, drawing an accurate graph or geometrical construction. Immediate feedback is provided on the formal completeness of solutions.

The general term for the input tools used in **ALEKS** is the "Answer Editor." This encompasses a variety of actual modes for user input: an Answer Editor for mathematical expressions, an Answer Editor for the numberline, and an Answer Editor for graphing in the Cartesian plane (with x and y coordinate axes). A student beginning to use **ALEKS** is thoroughly trained in all features of the Answer Editor

Key	Effect
Right arrow Tab Enter	moves the cursor one place to the right (ahead)
Left arrow	moves the cursor one place to the left (back)
Backspace	deletes input immediately preceding (to the left of) the cursor and moves the cursor one place to the left (back) OR deletes selected input

Figure 3.3: Using Special Keys in the Answer Editor

that are relevant to the subject being studied during the Tutorial (Sec. 2.8).

In much of what follows, emphasis is on the "Answer Editor for mathematical expressions," as this is the section which involves the greatest degree of interplay between mouse, keyboard, and on-screen buttons and icons.

3.5.1 Manipulators for Mathematical Expressions

The Answer Editor for Mathematical Expressions

The Answer Editor for mathematical expressions consists of two parts: a rectangular field into which mathematical expressions are entered (the "entry field") is to the left, and a "keypad" made of buttons with mathematical symbols is to the right (Fig. 3.1). These buttons have labels in the Tutorial, but do not thereafter. Mathematical expressions are entered and edited using the buttons of the Answer Editor keypad, as well as the basic keyboard, the Left and Right arrow keys, the Tab, Enter, and Backspace keys, and the mouse. **NOTE:** Buttons are displayed to correspond with the kind of problem being solved. The selection is made in such a way as to avoid giving away the correct answer. Keyboard shortcuts (Fig. 3.2) work only when the corresponding button is displayed.

Basic Input

When a new page is opened and contains a problem whose solution is a mathematical expression, the entry field initially contains at least one blue box. Each blue box represents a mathematical expression that forms part of the complete answer. To enter a mathematical expression one must first click on a blue box. When this is done, the cursor (or "caret") appears inside the box. The cursor marks the point at which something is entered. Material can be entered using the basic keyboard or the buttons of the keypad. Individual digits can be entered only from the keyboard. Symbols can be entered using the buttons of the keypad and, sometimes, from the keyboard as well (Fig. 3.2).

Basic Editing Tools

The cursor, showing the point at which material is entered, can be moved using the Left and Right arrows and the Tab and Enter keys. It can also be positioned using the mouse. Input can be deleted using the Backspace key. The effect of special keys is summarized in Fig. 3.3.

Selecting Input

It is possible to select a continuous portion of input by dragging the pointer with the mouse button held down. A segment that has been selected by dragging in this way can be deleted by pressing Backspace, replaced by typing, or replaced by clicking the buttons of the Answer Editor keypad. It can also be inserted into a mathematical expression such as a fraction or a square root (the selected portion is placed in the numerator position or under the square root sign, respectively).

Clear & Undo

After material has been entered the field can be returned to its empty state by clicking on "Clear." Clicking on "Undo" cancels the most recent action. Clicking on "Undo" a second time restores the effect of the canceled action (including a "Clear" command).

3.5.2   Mathematical Expressions

The purpose of the Answer Editor for mathematical expressions is to process user input in the form of syntactically correct mathematical expressions. One important way in which the Answer Editor guides the user in constructing such expressions is by means of the blue boxes. If a blue box remains on the screen, it is clear that the input type so far is not valid. If no blue boxes remain it may or may not be valid.

Entering expressions from the keyboard

For expressions that do not require the use of the Answer Editor keypad, the user can place the cursor within a blue box and enter the mathematical expression from the keyboard. For many expressions, however, the Answer Editor keypad must be used. It may be used, as well, for some types of expressions that can also be entered from the regular keyboard (Fig. 3.2).

Using the Answer Editor keypad to structure simple expressions

To form a simple mathematical expression, the user places the cursor in an empty blue box and clicks on the appropriate button from the Answer Editor keypad. The initial blue box disappears and new blue boxes may appear (depending on the button), accompanied by all of the necessary signs. The user can now fill in the new boxes.

Entering complex expressions

Sometimes it is necessary to enter more complex mathematical expressions. What has been written about entering mathematical expressions into a single blue box holds equally true for entering expressions into any of the blue boxes produced by clicking a button of the Answer Editor keypad. One can place the cursor in one of these boxes and enter an expression from the keyboard, or, by clicking on a button of the Answer Editor keypad, replace it with the structure of a new mathematical expression. Expressions of any degree of complexity can be created in this way.

NOTE: The Answer Editor does not supply parentheses. The user must know when these are necessary. In particular, when there is an expression consisting of more than one symbol that must be raised to a power, one may need to enclose it in parentheses, just as in writing; otherwise, only the final symbol (just before the exponent) will be raised to the specified power.

Alternate ways of entering expressions

The buttons of the Answer Editor keypad can be used in other ways as well. In particular, one can select some portion of the input in the entry field which constitutes a complete mathematical expression, and then click on a keypad button. This will create a new mathematical expression within which the expression selected is one component. The same basic rule applies: the minimum unit of manipulation is a complete mathematical expression.

Other mathematical signs

The following mathematical signs can be entered only from the keyboard:

- the plus sign (+);
- the minus sign (-), both for connecting the two parts of a subtraction expression and for designating a negative number;
- the period (.) used in decimals;
- the comma (,) used to punctuate numbers of more than three places.

Please note as well the following special cases:

The asterisk for multiplication

The "x" character on the keyboard cannot be used to enter a multiplication sign. Only the asterisk (*) serves this purpose. (The multiplication sign on the Answer Editor keypad, however, is the traditional x-shaped symbol.)

Mixed numbers

Although fractions can be entered from the keyboard using the front slash character (/), mixed numbers *cannot* be entered this way. More precisely, the Answer Editor does not automatically regard a whole number followed by a fraction as a mixed number. The mixed number button on the Answer Editor keypad *must* be used to enter mixed numbers.

3.5.3 Types of Mathematical Expressions

The following set of tips is intended to illustrate the variety of ways in which mathematical expressions can be entered using the Answer Editor. It is in no way a thorough description of the Answer Editor, which includes many other kinds of mathematical expressions and constructions.

Here, "Button" will always refer to a button on the Answer Editor keypad. By "select" we mean drag the mouse over the expression to be selected with the mouse button depressed, so that a red box appears surrounding it.

Square Root $\sqrt{81}$

- Click on the square root button and enter the expression into the square root sign; **OR**
- Enter the expression you wish to appear under the square root sign, select it, and click on the square root button.

In the simple example just given the second method reverses the sequence of steps of the first method. Such complementary methods are typical.

Absolute Value $|-6|$

- Click on the absolute value button and enter the expression whose absolute value you wish to express; **OR**
- Enter the expression whose absolute value you wish to express, select it, and click on the absolute value button.

Repeating Decimal $1.\overline{27}$

- Enter all digits that precede the repeating pattern, including the decimal point (a period on the keyboard) and any decimal places preceding the pattern, click on the bar button, and enter the repeating pattern; **OR**
- Enter all digits, including the decimal point (a period on the keyboard) and all decimal positions following it, select the repeating pattern only, and click on the bar button.

Exponent 3^2

- Click on the Exponent button, enter the base, then move the cursor to the exponent box and enter the exponent; **OR**
- Enter the expression you wish to raise to a power, click on the exponent button, and enter the exponent.

NOTE: If the number you wish to raise to a power is an expression consisting of more than one symbol, it may need to be enclosed in parentheses. The Answer Editor will not do this for you. If no parentheses are used, only the last symbol will be raised to a power.

Square Root Preceded by Multiplier $2\sqrt{6}$

With more complex expressions you can use the mouse to place the cursor in the needed position, as in the second method:

- Enter the multiplier, click on the square root button, and enter the expression you wish to be under the square root sign; **OR**

- Click on the square root button, click to the left of the square root sign, enter the multiplier, tab (or press the right arrow, or press Enter, or click on the blue box under the square root sign), and enter the expression you wish to be under the square root sign.

Percentage   48%

The next example illustrates the possibility, in some cases, of using either the Answer Editor keypad or the regular keyboard to enter signs:

- Enter the expression you wish to express as a percentage and click on the percent button; **OR**
- Enter the expression you wish to express as a percentage and then enter the (keyboard) percent sign.

Fraction $\frac{7}{10}$

Fractions can be entered conveniently at least three ways:

- Enter the numerator, enter a (keyboard) forward slash character, and enter the denominator; **OR**
- Enter the numerator, click on the fraction button, and enter the denominator; **OR**
- Click on the fraction button, enter the numerator, then click on the blue square in the position of the denominator and enter the denominator.

Mixed Number $5\frac{7}{8}$

Mixed numbers can be entered in more than one way, but they each require use of the mixed number button:

- Enter the whole number part, click on the mixed number button, enter the numerator, press Enter, and enter the denominator; **OR**
- Click on the mixed number button, click on the first blue box (for the whole part), enter the whole number part, press the right arrow, enter the numerator, move the cursor to the denominator position, and enter the denominator (i.e., fill in the boxes).

Fraction in square root followed by multiplier $\sqrt{\frac{5}{8}} \times 3$

For this example only one input method is given, but others can clearly be suggested:

- Click on the square root sign button, click on the fraction button, enter the numerator, tab, enter the denominator, then tab, enter an asterisk (from the keyboard), and enter the multiplier.

List $1, 2, 3$

For the purposes of the following example, assume that there is a list consisting of three components to be entered:

- Enter the first expression, click on the list button (or press the keyboard comma), enter the second expression, click on the list button, enter the third expression, click on the list button, and enter the fourth expression; **OR**

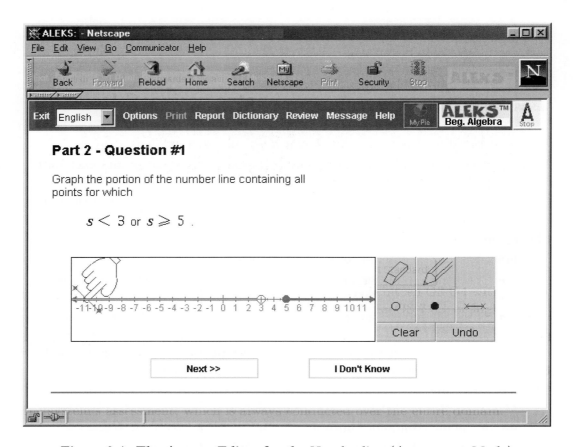

Figure 3.4: The Answer Editor for the Numberline (Assessment Mode)

- Click on the list button (or press the keyboard comma) twice, click on the first blue box, enter the first expression, move the cursor right, enter the second expression, move the cursor right, and enter the third expression.

Answers with Units   **10 cups**

Finally, there are some cases where the Answer Editor does part of the formatting. For example, in problems where answers must be expressed in some kind of units, such as dollars or candies, the unit expression needed may appear in advance.

3.5.4   The Answer Editor for the Numberline

The Answer Editor for the numberline consists of a numberline and tools for placing full and empty endpoints and segments (Fig. 3.4). To place a segment, mark a point on the numberline with the pencil, then click on that point with either the full or the empty tool. To place a segment, use the Region tool to click on any point in the relevant part of the numberline. If the user clicks between two endpoints the

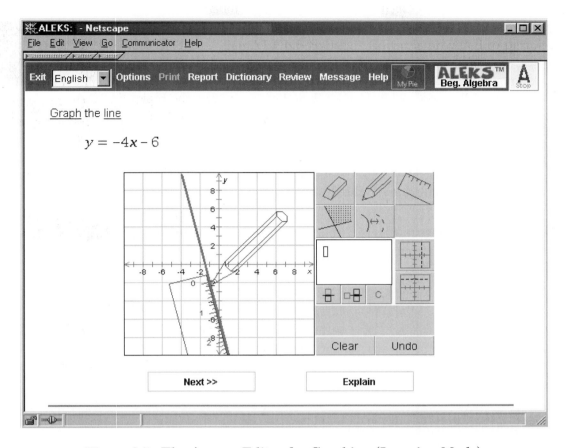

Figure 3.5: The Answer Editor for Graphing (Learning Mode)

segment will extend to each of them. When the user clicks between an endpoint and an extremity of the numberline the segment will appear with an arrow to indicate that it continues to infinity. The eraser will remove any part of the construction by clicking on it.

3.5.5   The Answer Editor for Graphing

The Answer Editor for graphing consists of a Cartesian plane with x and y coordinate axes and a selection of other tools for graphing lines and regions of the plane (Fig. 3.5).

- To graph a line, use the pencil tool to plot two points. Then, align the straightedge (ruler) on the two points (it is a "grabby" tool and will jump to a point when it is near it). Then use the pencil tool to draw the line. Note that the effect of the straightedge continues past its ends, so there is no need to move it to make a line going from edge to edge of the depicted plane.

- To fill in a region, use the region tool and click in the desired region of the plane. One must draw all lines defining the region before filling it in. In order for one or more of the lines defining a region to be dotted (as in the graph of a system containing one or more strict inequalities), click on the line with the dotted line tool. This may be done before or after the region is filled.

- To place a point where coordinates are not both integers: use the small input field to enter numerical values (fractions and mixed numbers can be placed using the icons beneath the field), then click on the icons for "graph x" and "graph y." A dotted line will appear on the plane for each given coordinate. Use the pencil to mark the desired point at their intersection.

As with the numberline, select the eraser tool click on any part of a line, arc, or other component to remove it.

3.6   Assessment Report

At the conclusion of an assessment, the Assessment Report is presented. The interpretation of this report is the same as for piechart displays found in other places within **ALEKS** (such as in "MyPie").

3.6.1   Standard Report Format

The standard report format is used for all assessment reports. This format consists of one or more piecharts (Fig. 3.6).

3.6.2   Interpreting the Piecharts

Piecharts express the results of a given assessment. They contain the following types of information:

- which general topics of the mathematics curriculum are part of the syllabus;
- the relative importance of the parts of the mathematics syllabus; and
- to what extent the student has attained the knowledge for each part of the mathematics syllabus, according to the assessment.

Each color-coded slice of the piechart refers to a particular part of the syllabus, such as "Whole Numbers" or "Proportions and Percents." Each slice is marked with an abbreviation. The meanings of these abbreviations and of the chart's color-coding are given in the legend immediately following the piechart. If the abbreviation next

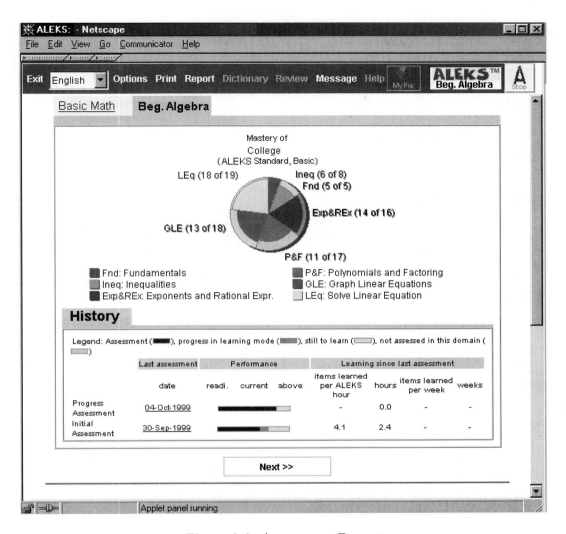

Figure 3.6: Assessment Report

to the slice is underlined, it means this topic contains concepts the student is most "ready to learn."

A piechart will show only those topics that are part of the math curriculum for the course indicated. The portion of the chart taken up by any one topic reflects the importance of that topic relative to others in the given syllabus.

The progress a student has made toward satisfying the syllabus goals for knowledge in a given topic is expressed by the degree to which the slice corresponding to that area is shaded (i.e., filled in with solid color). The measure of progress given by the piecharts is dependent on the standards for a particular course and is set by instructors and administrators (Chap. 6).

When a user places the pointer over one of the slices of the pie charts, the slice pops out of the pie. A list of the items for that topic the student is currently best ready to learn will appear. Not every slice necessarily contains such a list, even if the topic has not yet been fully mastered. If the slice contains concepts, its label is underlined. This is because a student may not be ready to learn a concept in a given topic (slice) before concepts in another topic (slice) have been mastered. Clicking on any one of these concepts takes the user into the Learning Mode, beginning with that concept.

3.6.3   Multiple Piecharts

When a course is part of an integrated sequence, one or two additional piecharts may appear. They represent the previous and/or subsequent courses in the sequence.

3.6.4   Ready to Learn

The concepts given as most "ready to learn" do not represent a casual selection of concepts that the student has not yet mastered. By resuming study with one of these concepts, the student is following the most efficient path to mastery of the complete domain (Chap. 8).

3.6.5   Progress Bars

Another graphic expression of the student's progress is given by the bar graphs at the bottom of the report ("History"). These represent the general extent of the student's mastery: the blue portion of each bar represents material that was learned as of the given assessment, the green portion material mastered in the Learning Mode since that assessment, and the yellow portion material belonging to the curriculum for the given level that has yet to be learned. When the bar is entirely blue, the student has completed the curriculum for a level or levels.

Chapter 4

Learning Module

4.1 The ALEKS Learning Mode

The purpose of the Learning Mode is to assist students in mastering mathematical concepts. Students using **ALEKS** choose which concepts they wish to work on in the Learning Mode from the list of concepts the system has determined they are most prepared to learn. This happens either as the result of an assessment or through the continuous update of assessment results that is performed by the Learning Module. Students in the Learning Mode work on those concepts they are best prepared to learn so that the benefit of their work is maximized.

In the Learning Mode students always work on one particular concept at a time. The Learning Mode provides them with a rich array of resources to help in mastering this concept. This includes explanations, references to a McGraw-Hill textbook if one is being used in conjunction with **ALEKS**, links to supplemental tutorial material and interactive applications, practice problems, diagnostic feedback on problem solutions, and access to a student mathematical Dictionary. Moreover, the Learning Module is designed to monitor the progress made by students toward mastery of a given concept and advise them on continuing or changing concepts. A student is required to solve an appropriate number of practice problems correctly before the system will conclude that the concept has been mastered. At this point the student is encouraged to choose a new concept from the (updated) piechart, but the opportunity to continue to work on this concept is available if the student wishes. If the student makes mistakes, a greater number of correct solutions may be required. If the student has continued difficulty, the system may suggest closer attention to the explanations or offer the name of a classmate who has recently mastered this concept. If the student appears frustrated by the present concept, a new selection will be offered.

The student continues to work in the Learning Mode until a new assessment is

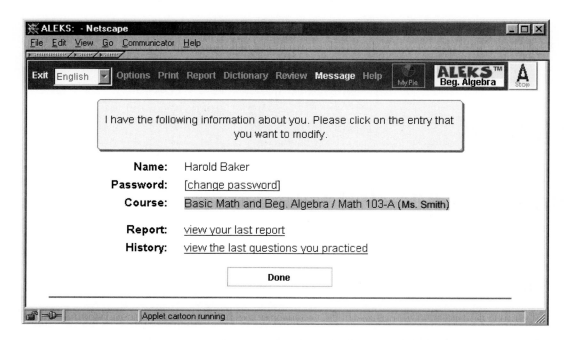

Figure 4.1: The Options Page (Learning Module)

ordered, either by the instructor or automatically (when a certain amount of time has been spent or a certain amount of progress has been made since the last assessment; Sec. 3.3).

4.2   Menus

The following sections describe buttons available on the Menu Bar in the Learning Module.

4.2.1   Exit

One can end a session with **ALEKS** in either of two ways: click on the "Exit" button at the upper left-hand corner of the browser window or simply close the window in one of the ways provided by the browser. Also, if no input is supplied to the system for 15 minutes the session is terminated automatically. No matter which way you exit, **ALEKS** will return you to the same place when you next log on.

4.2.2   Options

The "Options" button opens a page containing the user's current registration information, with a link for changing the Password (Fig. 4.1). "Report" connects to a menu of all assessment reports (Sec. 4.2.4). "History" displays a list of concepts the student has worked on recently, indicating the level of mastery achieved and providing the opportunity to return to that concept for further practice (Sec. 4.2.6). Clicking on "Done" returns to the Learning Mode.

4.2.3   Print

To print the contents of the **ALEKS** display, click the "Print" button on the menu bar. This transforms the display into a form suitable for printing. Next, click on the browser's "Print" button, or use whatever keyboard equivalent is provided. The procedure is the same as for printing any web page. To return to the Learning Mode, close or minimize the window that was printed.

4.2.4   Report

Clicking on the "Report" button displays a menu of all past assessments, with the most recent displayed by default. Any assessment can be selected (by date) from the menu. Then click "Graph" to see the results of that assessment. This will include one or more piecharts, a list of concepts recently learned, a list of concepts most ready to be learned, and the progress bar graphs (Sec. 3.6.5). To return to the Learning Mode, click "Done."

4.2.5   Dictionary

Clicking on this button produces a new browser window with an index of entries in the online student mathematics Dictionary. Click on any entry to view the definition. Remember that the Dictionary can also be accessed by clicking on underlined words (hypertext links) anywhere in the Learning Mode. Dictionary definitions are designed to present concepts in their simplest form first, moving into greater depth as the definition proceeds (Sec. 4.3.5). Close or minimize the Dictionary window to return to the Learning Mode.

4.2.6   Review

The "Review" button gives a list of concepts the student has recently worked on in the Learning Mode. One can click any of these concepts to get further practice on it. There is also an option for "more extensive review." Click on "Done" to return to the Learning Mode.

NOTE: The system will sometimes automatically offer a student the option of reviewing past material at the time of login.

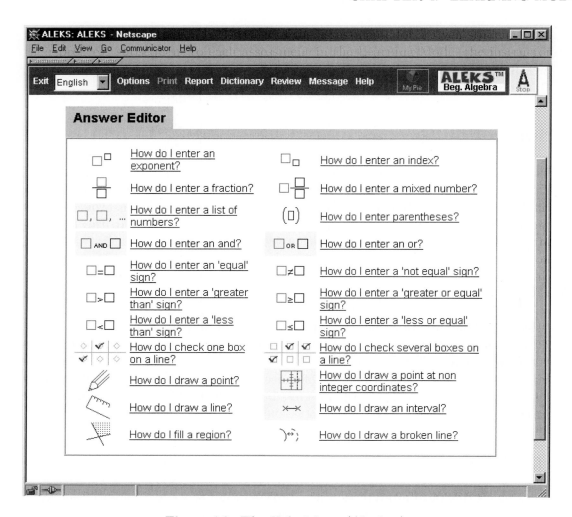

Figure 4.2: The Help Menu (Algebra)

4.2.7   Message

The student can use this button to check for messages from the instructor or administrator, and respond to messages if this has been enabled. Click on "Done" to return to the Learning Mode.

4.2.8   Help

The "Help" button in the Assessment and Learning Modes provides detailed assistance with use of the Answer Editor (Fig. 4.2). The Help Menu contains a list of questions on how to use the various icons of the Answer Editor; clicking any one of these leads to a brief refresher tutorial on the use of the icon.

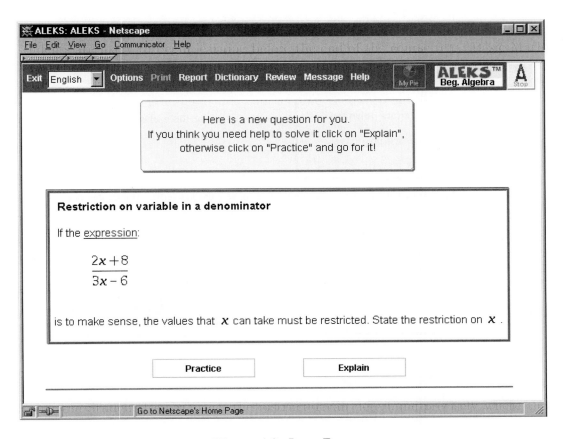

Figure 4.3: Item Page

4.2.9 MyPie

Clicking on "MyPie" produces a piechart display reflecting the current state of the student's mastery in the Learning Mode (Sec. 3.6). The student can use this button to select a new concept to work on from among those currently most "ready to learn."

4.3 The Learning Mode Interface

4.3.1 Item Page

The item page contains the title of the current item, such as "Absolute Value of a Negative Integer," followed by a problem or *instance* of that item (Fig. 4.3). Mathematical terms are underlined and set off as hyperlinks (clicking on these will open the Dictionary). There is, however, no Answer Editor: the answer to the problem must be given on the Practice page.

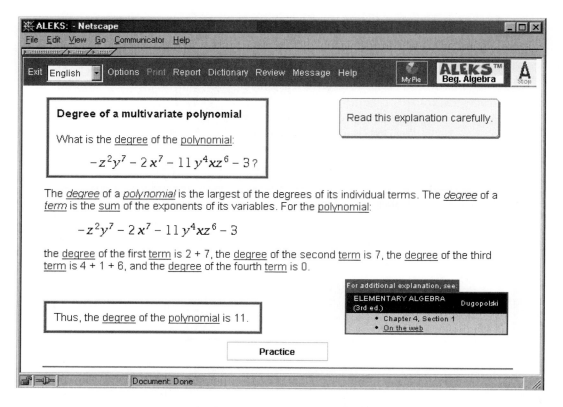

Figure 4.4: Explanation Page

Underneath the problem are two buttons, "Practice" and "Explain." Clicking on "Explain" goes to a detailed explanation of the item with additional Dictionary links. Clicking on "Practice" goes to a page containing the Answer Editor and provides the opportunity to attempt solving the problem.

4.3.2   Explanation Page

Like the item page, the explanation page (Fig. 4.4) begins with the title of the current item and an instance of that item (the same one that appeared on the item page, but rephrased and sometimes accompanied by a hint). The answer to the problem is supplied at the end of the explanation.

When **ALEKS** is used with a McGraw-Hill textbook, a reference will appear at the bottom of the explanation page giving the chapter and section of the textbook where additional explanation of the concept may be found. Additional tutorial material and interactive applications may also be found through links at the bottom of the explanation page.

Here again, mathematical terms are linked to Dictionary definitions. The system

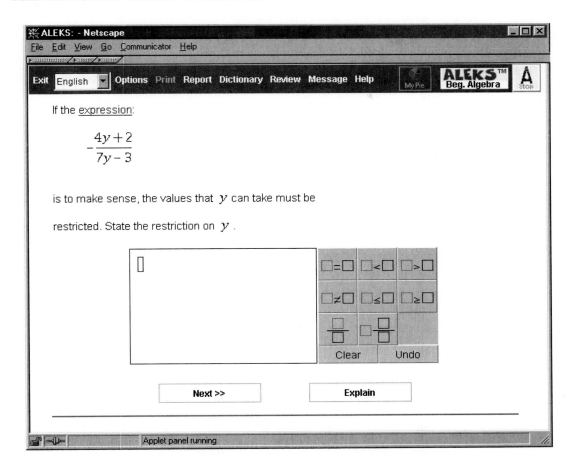

Figure 4.5: Practice Page

may suggest looking up certain key terms to help with the explanation (especially if the explanation has already been visited). At the bottom of the page is the "Practice" button. Clicking on this button produces a new instance of the same problem-type.

4.3.3 Practice Page

This page displays an instance of the problem, followed by the Answer Editor. This is where a solution to the problem can be attempted (Fig. 4.5). All practice problems are generated by algorithms with random selection of numerical values so that the variety of problem instances for any item is very great.

Underneath the Answer Editor are buttons labeled "Next" and "Explain." Clicking on "Next" has the same effect described in the Assessment Mode: it submits the answer. Here, however, the user finds out immediately whether the answer is right or wrong. If it was correct, a new problem is presented or (if the system believes this

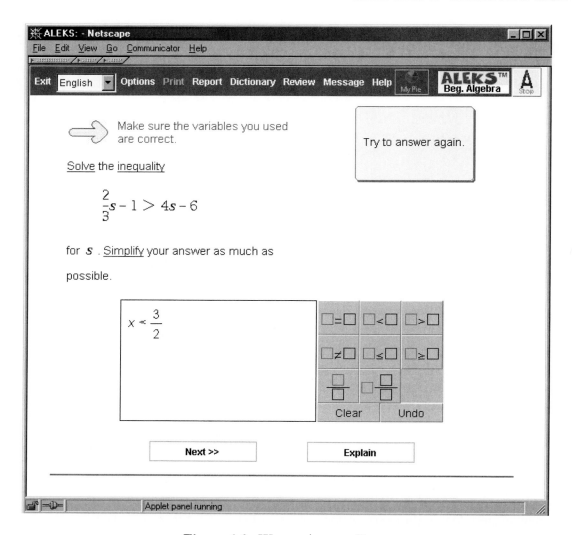

Figure 4.6: Wrong Answer Page

topic has been mastered) a choice of new items is offered. Wrong answers will bring about presentation of the same problem (on the Wrong Answer page) with feedback on the student's error. Students can then click on "Explain." At the explanation page, the problem is rephrased and often a hint is given.

4.3.4 Wrong Answer Page

The wrong answer page appears only after an incorrect answer has been submitted on the practice page (Fig. 4.6). It is identical to the previous page except that the system explains the answer is wrong, and offers advice on what went wrong and which words might be looked up in the Dictionary.

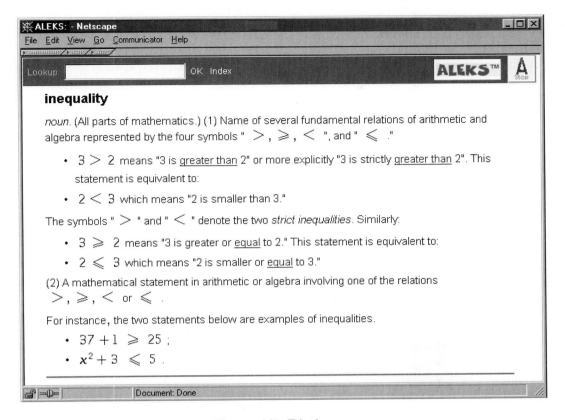

Figure 4.7: Dictionary

The old, incorrect answer appears in the Answer Editor, where it can be corrected and resubmitted. Again, clicking on "Explain" is an option that leads to an explanation of the problem.

4.3.5 Dictionary

The online mathematics dictionary is always available in the Learning Mode. In addition to the Dictionary menu (button), links to the Dictionary appear in explanations, item descriptions, and in the feedback.

Clicking on a link to the Dictionary creates a new window on top of the **ALEKS** interface. At the top of the window is a bar with an Index button and text entry field (Fig. 4.7). The "Index" button gives access to an index of all the Dictionary's headings and subheadings. Beneath this bar is the Dictionary entry, with links to other entries and graphic illustrations as appropriate. The window can be closed after use or minimized for quicker access the next time needed.

4.4 Feedback in Learning Mode

In the Learning Mode feedback is integrated into a sophisticated system of guidance for the student. Some errors prompt **ALEKS** to give specific hints and suggestions (Fig. 4.6). Some examples: it may say a fractional answer needs to be reduced or that a list of expressions is incomplete. After a right answer the system will ask a limited number of questions for the same concept before judging that it has been mastered. If an item is missed too many times, however, a new topic will be suggested. This teaching strategy attempts to minimize frustration and keep the student's head clear. If a concept has been left without mastery being attained, however, the system may suggest returning to it after one or two other topics have been covered.

4.5 Ask a Friend

Under some circumstances, a button marked "Ask a Friend" will appear at the bottom of the page in the Learning Mode, next to the "Explain" button. Clicking on this button enables the student to ask for help from another student using **ALEKS** in the same course.

The button appears only if (1) the instructor has made this feature active, (2) the student was unsuccessful in answering this concept, and (3) there is another student who has successfully answered the concept and who has chosen to participate in the "Ask a Friend" component.

Chapter 5

Instructor/Administrator Module: Results & Progress

5.1 The ALEKS Instructor Module

The Instructor Module provides features to assist instructors in monitoring and managing their courses and individual students using **ALEKS**. Any registered instructor logging on to **ALEKS** enters the Instructor Module automatically. The Instructor Module contains a great variety of tools and facilities. Some may seldom be needed. It is essential, however, that any instructor using **ALEKS** be familiar with the Instructor Module to be able to monitor individual and group progress, check assessment reports, and request assessments.

5.2 Access to the Instructor Module

When you log on to **ALEKS** using the Login Name and Password assigned to you as an instructor or administrator you will automatically enter the Instructor Module. If you have an instructor account you will see a directory containing only your own courses. If you have an administrator account you will see all of the instructor directories for your college. If you have a root administrator account you will see directories for all colleges under your administration (Fig. 5.1).

If you have an instructor account, the system features at your disposal can affect only your classes and the students under your supervision. If your account is that of an institutional administrator, your privileges are similar, but extend to all the classes and all the students in the college. If your account is that of a root administrator (e.g., over a multi-campus community college system), your privileges extend to all colleges under your administration. In the following, we assume that your account is that of an institutional administrator.

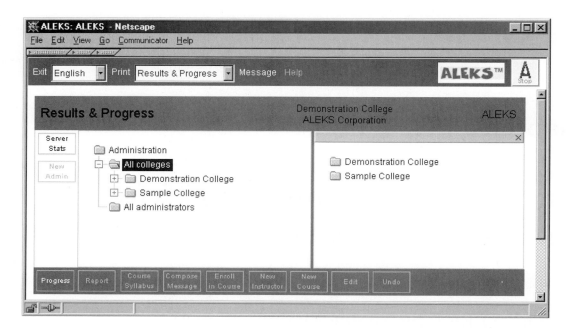

Figure 5.1: The Results & Progress Directory (Instructor Module)

The Instructor Module has two parts: "Results & Progress" and "Standards & Syllabi." When you enter the Instructor Module you are automatically placed in Results & Progress. Use the **ALEKS** menu bar to change the part of the Instructor Module in which you are working (Chap. 6).

"Results & Progress" is used for most administrative tasks, such as monitoring individual and group progress. Instructors using **ALEKS** with one or more courses will probably wish to check into this part of the Instructor Module on a daily basis. This allows the instructors to verify the rate of progress achieved by the students. The features also enable instructors to set up additional classes if they need to.

The following sections describe the various actions that can be carried out by instructors with appropriate levels of privilege in the Instructor Module.

5.3 View Student Progress

To view student progress, select the name of the student and click on the "Progress" button. A chart will appear below the directories window with one or more rows of information (Fig. 5.2). There is one row for each assessment that the student has taken, with dates (linked to the Report page for that assessment). Each row contains one to three bar graphs, depending on the student's level. Each bar graph measures the student's mastery as of the given assessment as seen by the blue portion of the bar. Progress made in the Learning Mode subsequently to that assessment (but

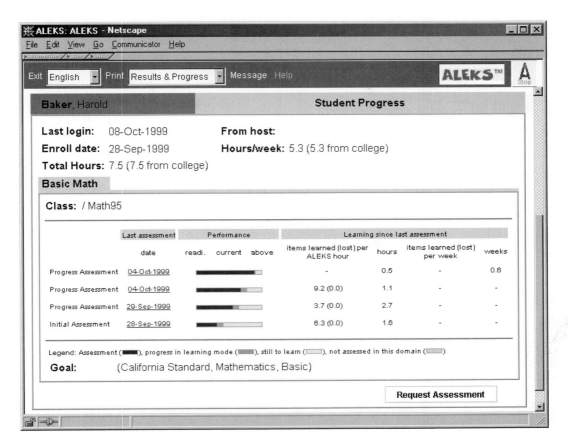

Figure 5.2: Student Progress (Instructor Module)

before the next assessment, if there is one) is measured by the green portion of the bar. If there is more than one bar per row, they will correspond to the syllabi for the previous level, the current level, and the subsequent level.

A variety of other information, clearly labeled, is provided on the Progress page: date of last login, enrollment date, total hours spent on the system. Information on each assessment, total hours and weeks spent subsequently in the Learning Mode (up to the time of the next assessment) with average numbers of items gained per hour and per week is also provided. There is also a button which the instructor can use to schedule an assessment for this student.

Monitoring progress: When a student has spent enough time on **ALEKS** to have had two or more assessments, the sequence of bar graphs appearing on the Student Progress page begins to tell a clear story of the student's success in moving toward mastery. Be warned that there is considerable difference among individual students in the speed and smoothness of the progress that you will see here. When one bar graph appears above another bar graph, the uppermost one represents a later

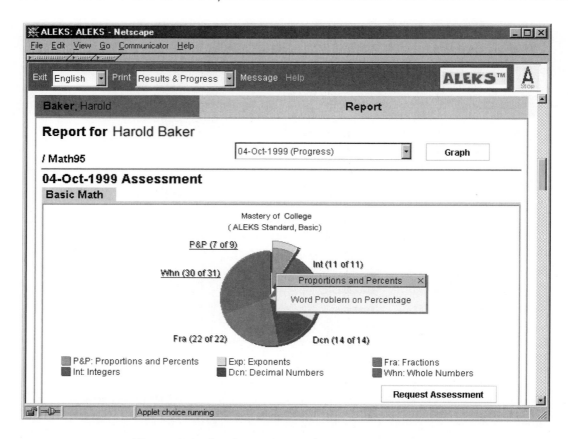

Figure 5.3: Student Report (Instructor Module)

assessment, in which the student seeks to confirm knowledge of material tentatively mastered in Learning Mode. For some students progress in assessments is slower than that in Learning Mode. This can be seen when the green portion of one bar graph extends further to the right than the blue portion of the bar graph above it (not everything covered in Learning Mode was confirmed subsequently in the assessment). For other students the opposite is true: progress in assessments is for some reason faster than that in the Learning Mode. This can be seen when the green portion of one bar graph does not extend so far to the right as the blue portion of the bar graph above it (more knowledge was confirmed in the assessment than had been covered previously in Learning Mode). Instructors who follow their students' work with **ALEKS** closely can hardly help being fascinated by these differences. When a student is frustrated, this will be obvious from the bar graphs; in such cases the instructor may need to provide extra help or encouragement. It is well worth the instructor's time to check daily on individual and course progress in **ALEKS** (Sec. 7.4).

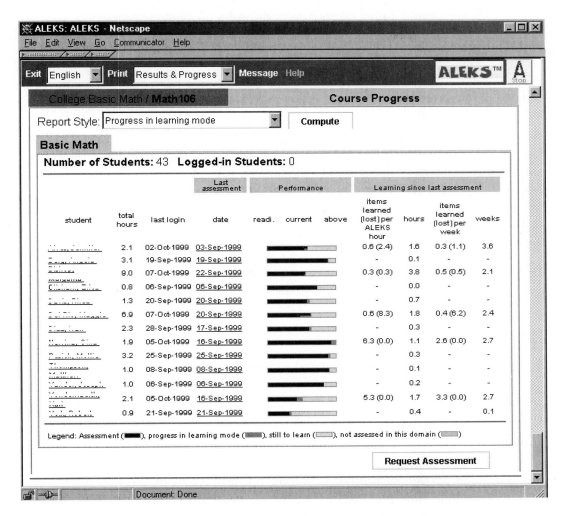

Figure 5.4: Course Progress (Instructor Module)

5.4   View Student Assessment Report

Select the name of the student for whom you wish to observe a report and click
on the "Report" button. A display containing one or more piecharts will appear
beneath the directories window (Fig. 5.3). Its interpretation is the same as for
the reports received by students following all formal assessments (Sec. 3.6.1). By
default, the most recent assessment is shown. Other assessments may be chosen by
selecting dates from the menu at the top of the chart and clicking on "Graph."

Beneath the piecharts are lists of concepts that the student has mastered recently,
and that the student is currently (as of the given assessment) most ready to begin
learning. There may also be a summary of the student's history in **ALEKS** ("History"), a log of responses on the given assessment ("Assessment log"), and a log of

work in the Learning Mode following that assessment ("Learning log"). There is also a button allowing the instructor to request an assessment for that student.

5.5   View Course Progress

Select the course for which you wish to observe progress and click on the "Progress" button. A chart will appear below the directories window with a series of rows, one for each student enrolled in the course (Fig. 5.4). The rows contain bar graphs (see interpretation in "View Student Progress," Sec. 5.3). At this point, only the bar graph for the most recent assessment is shown (the students' names are linked to their individual Progress pages, while the assessment dates are linked to their individual Report pages).

Display options: A range of options providing variations on this format are accessible through a menu at the top of the chart. Choose the desired format from the menu and click on "Compute" to view results.

Progress in Learning mode

All students who have completed at least one assessment have bar graphs. The blue portion of the bar graph shows mastery as of the most recent assessment, and the green portion shows progress in the Learning Mode since that assessment.

Total progress

All students who have completed at least two assessments have bar graphs. The blue portion of the bar graph shows mastery as of the first assessment, and the light blue portion shows progress made between that assessment and the most recent assessment taken.

Most recent progress

All students who have completed at least two assessments have bar graphs. The blue portion of the bar graph shows mastery as of the assessment immediately preceding the most recent one, and the light blue portion shows progress made between that assessment and the most recent assessment taken.

Progress over last 6 months

All students who have completed at least two assessments within the last six months have bar graphs. The blue portion of the bar graph shows mastery as of the first assessment taken within the last six months, and the light blue portion shows progress made between that assessment and the most recent one taken.

Progress over last 3 months

All students who have completed at least two assessments within the last three months have bar graphs. The blue portion of the bar graph shows mastery as

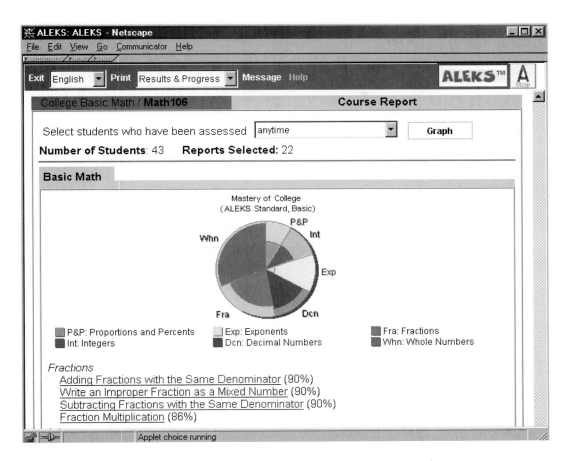

Figure 5.5: Course Report (Instructor Module)

of the first assessment taken within the last three months, and the light blue portion shows progress made between that assessment and the most recent one taken.

Progress over last month

All students who have completed at least two assessments within the last month have bar graphs. The blue portion of the bar graph shows mastery as of the first assessment taken within the last month, and the light blue portion shows progress made between that assessment and the most recent one taken.

Most recent assessment only

All students who have completed at least one assessment have bar graphs. The blue portion shows mastery as of the most recent assessment.

Finally, a button at the bottom of the page allows the instructor to schedule an assessment for all the students taking the course.

5.6   View Course Report

Select the course for which you wish to view a report and click on the "Report" button. A display containing one or more piecharts will appear beneath the directories window. Its interpretation is the same as for the reports received by students following all formal assessments, except that it represents a synthetic summary of reports received by all students in the course. The period summarized may be changed using the menu at the top of the chart (click on "Graph" to display results).

Display options: Beneath the piecharts there are other kinds of analysis available for class assessment data. Choose "Average" or "Ready to learn" from the "Display Mode" menu and click on "Graph" to display results.

Average

This option produces a list of the specific concepts mastered by a percentage of the students, as of their most recent assessment. The list is organized by general categories (Fig. 5.5). For each concept, the percentage of students in the course who demonstrated mastery is given.

Ready to learn

This option also shows a list of specific concepts, organized by general categories. For each concept, it shows the number of students in the course who are best ready to learn that concept, as of their most recent assessment. Clicking on a concept title will display a list of the students who are ready to learn it.

Focusing instruction: These tools can be used to focus instruction for courses and groups of students. The "Average" display shows very clearly which specific concepts and general areas within the syllabus need the most work for the greatest number of students. Consequently, it can be used to prioritize topics for lectures and lesson plans. The "Ready to learn" display, on the other hand, makes it possible to break a large course up into small groups, each focused on the concept or concepts that it is working on currently in Learning Mode. Where there is not sufficient teaching staff to coach several groups simultaneously, the instructor may call out small groups during their use of **ALEKS** for brief, pointed "chalk talks."

At the bottom of the Course Report page there is a button allowing the instructor to schedule an assessment for all the students in the course.

5.7   Schedule Student Assessment

Assessments for individual students may be requested using buttons on the Progress or Report pages for those students (Fig. 5.6). When the instructor has requested an assessment, the student will immediately enter the Assessment Mode at the next

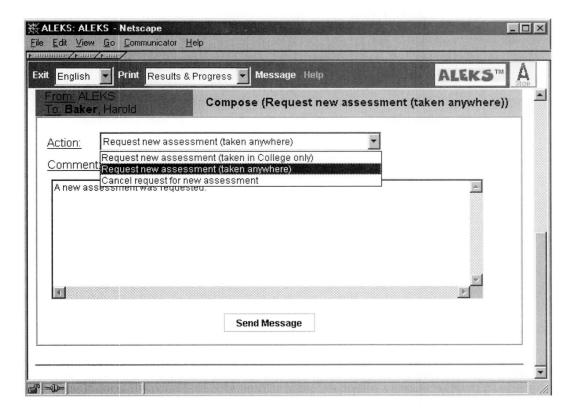

Figure 5.6: Student Assessment (Instructor Module)

login. The instructor can specify whether the assessment is to be taken from any location or only from the college.

NOTE: If an assessment is scheduled, whether by the instructor or automatically by the system, and the student is required to take the assessments at the college, the student will be unable to use the system from locations other than college until the assessment is completed (Sec. 5.14).

5.8 Schedule Course Assessment

Assessments for entire courses may be requested using buttons on the Progress or Report pages for those courses. When the instructor has scheduled an assessment, all students in the course will immediately enter the Assessment Mode at the next login. The instructor can specify whether the assessment is to be taken from any location or only from the college.

NOTE: If an assessment is scheduled, whether by the instructor or automatically by the system, and the student is required to take assessments at the college, the

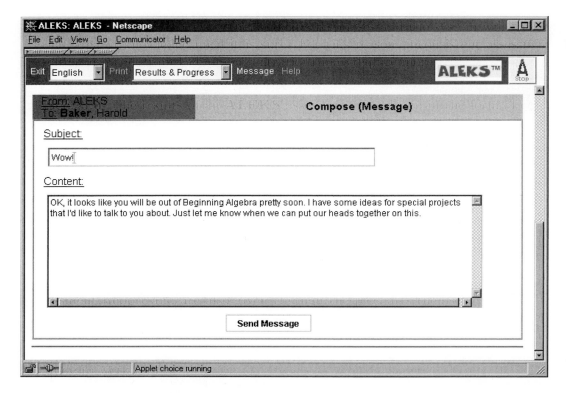

Figure 5.7: Send Message (Instructor Module)

student will be unable to use the system from locations other than college until the assessment is completed (Sec. 5.14).

5.9 Send Message

Select the student or course to whom you wish to send a message, and click on the "Compose Message" button. A simple editor will appear beneath the directories window with fields for a subject and a message and a "Send Message" button (Fig. 5.7). The student or students to whom the message is being sent will see it at their next login.

5.10 Check Messages

Click on the "Message" button at the top of the Instructor Module window. You can receive messages from students in a course only in response to your own messages, and then only if this has been enabled in the instructor account (Sec. 5.12).

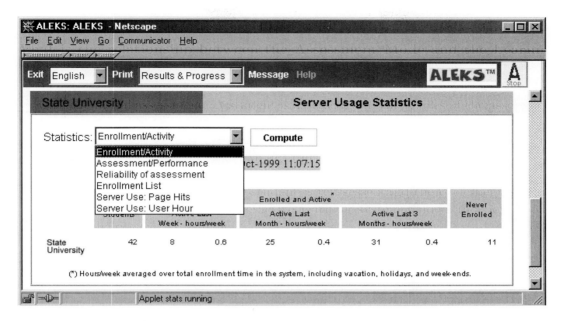

Figure 5.8: Server Statistics (Instructor Module)

5.11 Check Server Usage

Click on the "Server Stats" button. A table will appear beneath the directories window (Fig. 5.8). The type of information shown in the table can be changed by selecting a heading from the menu at the top of the table and clicking the "Compute" button. The options for display are: Enrollment/Activity, Assessment/Performance, Reliability of Assessment, Enrollment List, Server Use: Page Hits, Server Use: User Hours.

NOTE: The information provided by this feature is of interest to system administrators, instructors, and administrators seeking general statistical information on the use of **ALEKS**.

5.12 Create Instructor Account

Select the directory for the college where you wish to create an instructor account (or the directory "All instructors") and click on the "New Instructor" button. A form for the new account will appear beneath the directories window (Fig. 5.9). Supply the instructor's first and last names, a title ("Mr.," "Mrs.," "Ms.," "Prof."), a Login Name, and a Password. By default, the new account is set for an instructor. If you are an administrator you can make another administrator account by checking "Instructor and Administrator." The "ID" field is optional and may be left blank. "Message from student" should be enabled if you wish the account holder to have

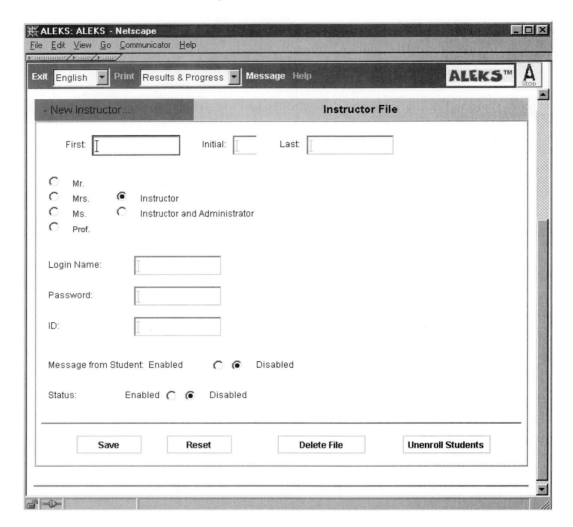

Figure 5.9: Instructor Account (Instructor Module)

access to messages from students. "Status" must be enabled if the instructor is to have courses assigned.

When you are finished filling in the form click on "Save." This creates the account. To start over click "Reset." To cancel the account click "Delete File."

5.13   Edit Instructor Account

Select the instructor whose account you wish to edit and click the "Edit" button. The same form will appear as described in "Create Instructor Account" (Fig. 5.9). The account may be deleted ("Delete File") only if there are no courses and no

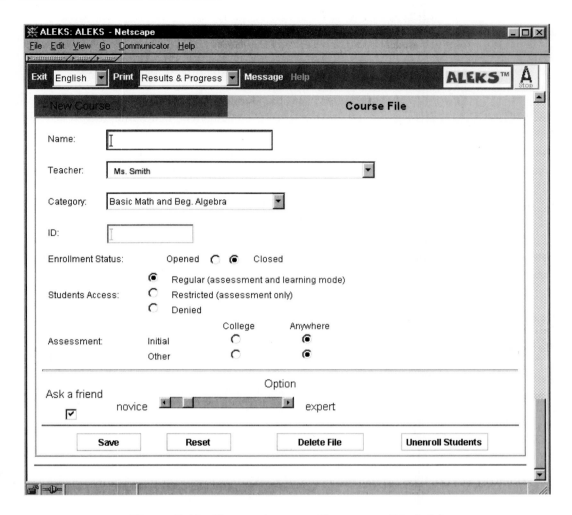

Figure 5.10: Course Account (Instructor Module)

students enrolled for this instructor ("Unenroll Students").

5.14 Create Course Account

Select the instructor for whom you wish to create a course and click on the "New Course" button. A form for the new account will appear beneath the directories window (Fig. 5.10). Provide a name (e.g., "Aleks") and choose a category ("Basic Math and Algebra," "Basic Math," or "Algebra"). At this point, you have the option of choosing an instructor other than the one initially selected (if others are available). This will transfer the course to that instructor. Set "Enrollment Status" to "Opened" if you wish to enroll students in this course. The "ID" field is optional and ordinarily left blank. "Students Access" is defaulted to the Assessment and

Learning Modes, and should be left that way except for special purposes. Similarly, assessments are permitted from any location by default. The instructor may wish to restrict the initial assessment so that it can be taken only at the college. Other assessments may be restricted in this way as well.

SUGGESTIONS: It is usually preferable to conduct the students' initial assessment as part of the general orientation to the **ALEKS** system and while under the instructor's supervision (Sec. 2.9). Experience has also shown that unless all the students in the course have clearly demonstrated their knowledge of Basic Math, they should initially be enrolled in a course for which the category "Basic Math" is set. This way the students can confirm their knowledge of all elements of Basic Math and be "graduated" to a new course for which the category "Algebra" is set. The students thus have a sense of accomplishment, and the instructor ensures that there is complete preparedness for Algebra, as defined in the system. The combined assessment for Basic Math and Algebra is naturally longer than for either of the two separately.

ASK A FRIEND: If this option is checked a student will be able to request the name of a classmate. "Novice" means the system will choose a classmate who has mastered the concept very recently. "Expert" means that the system will choose a classmate who mastered the concept earlier than others in the group. The instructor may pick any point on the continuum between "novice" and "expert."

When you are finished filling in the form click on "Save." This creates the account. To start over, click "Reset." To cancel the account click "Delete File."

5.15 Edit Course Account

Select the course you wish to edit and click on the "Edit" button. The same form will appear as described in "Create Course Account" (Fig. 5.10). The account may be deleted ("Delete File") only if there are no students currently enrolled in the course ("Unenroll Students").

5.16 Select Course Syllabus

Select the course for which you wish to select a syllabus and click on the "Select Course Syllabus" button. A form will appear beneath the directories window containing menus for all syllabi needed for the given course (Fig. 5.11). When you are finished filling in the form click on "Save." To start over or restore defaults click on "Reset."

NOTE: A course "syllabus" is a selection of concepts used as a goal for mastery by the students in a given course (Chap. 6). In college courses a single set is chosen

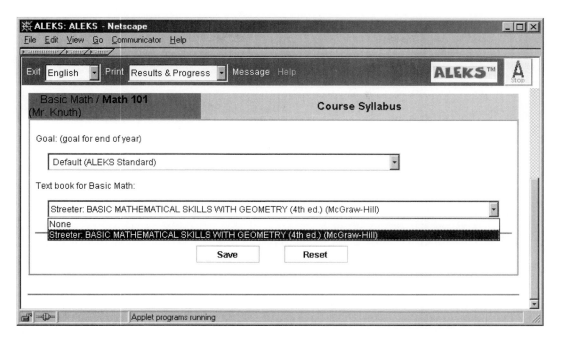

Figure 5.11: Course Syllabus (Instructor Module)

for the course. Syllabi belong to "standards," or sets of syllabi covering a range of levels, and are set to appropriate defaults. Thus, in most cases the instructor need not select a course syllabus.

5.17 Enroll and Unenroll Students

Select the course for which you wish to enroll or unenroll students and click on "Enroll in Course." A display will appear beneath the directories window showing the names of all students who may be enrolled. The currently enrolled students appear with their names highlighted. Students enrolled in another course, and so ineligible to be enrolled in this one, have a small "(o)" following their names. The names of students can be highlighted (enrolled) or dehighlighted (unenrolled) by clicking on them. Students enrolled in another class must be unenrolled from that class before they can be enrolled in this one. When all desired changes have been made, click on the "Save" button.

To move students from one class to another, they must first be unenrolled from the old class, and then reenrolled in the new class.

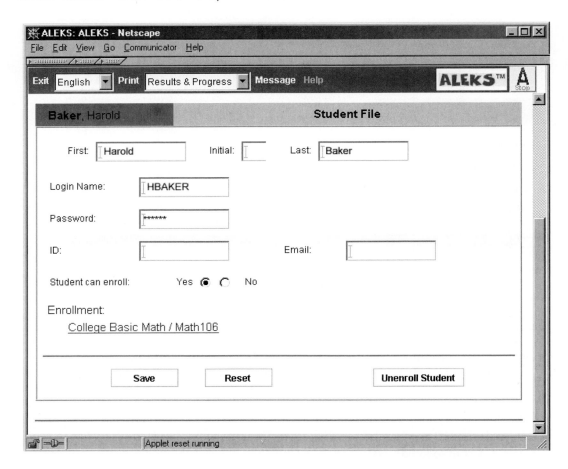

Figure 5.12: Student Account (Instructor Module)

5.18   Edit Student Account

To edit a student account, select the name of the student and click on the "Edit" button. A form will appear beneath the directories window containing the student's account information: name, level, login name, ID, email, and current enrollment status (Fig. 5.12). The student's Password is not shown in a readable form, but it can be changed to provide a student with a new Password when one has been forgotten. Corrections or changes may also be made to the student's name, level, login name, ID, and email. The student's ID and email are optional, though it may be useful to have the latter on record.

Chapter 6

Instructor/Administrator Module: Standards & Syllabi

By default, the Instructor Module displays "Results & Progress," as described in the preceding sections (Chap. 5). A second mode, "Standards & Syllabi," can be chosen from the menu at the top of the Instructor Module window (Fig. 6.1). This mode enables instructors to explore the system of standards and syllabi currently available in their **ALEKS** database. Administrators with a sufficiently high level of user privilege may also copy syllabi and standards, and modify them to suit the needs of a college. At the college level, the goals of courses in mathematics usually correspond to the entire subject matter, so that editing syllabi is seldom necessary.

A "syllabus," in the parlance of the **ALEKS** system, is a set of concepts taken from the sum total of concepts defining mastery of a domain (e.g., Basic Math or Algebra) that has been set as the curricular goal for a particular level of study. That is to say, mastery of this set of concepts is equivalent to completion of the curriculum for that level, and all reports generated by the system for students and courses using this syllabus are framed in terms of the syllabus. A "standard" is a set of syllabi covering a range of levels, such as might be published by a government educational authority.

To view a particular standard or syllabus, use the directories window of "Standards & Syllabi." This will open the folder for a particular level within a particular standard. Normally the syllabus will be organized by topics and subtopics using standard mathematical terminology. The syllabus is defined in terms of a list of individual concepts within these topics, each of which is either marked with a checkmark, indicating that it belongs to the syllabus, or not so marked. Editing a new standard means adding and removing checkmarks from individual "items" according to some schema of curricular progress.

NOTE: The syllabi selected for use by particular courses in **ALEKS** do not affect

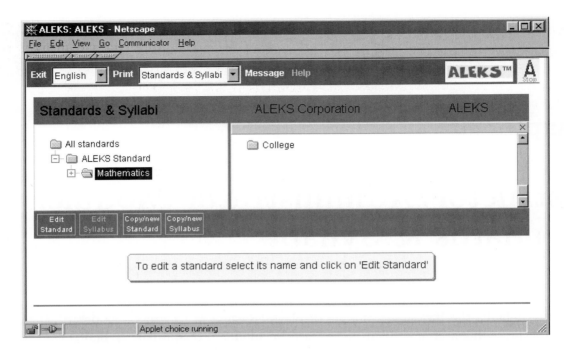

Figure 6.1: The Standards & Syllabi Directory (Instructor Module)

the system's assessment, which is always conducted over the entire domain.

6.1   Items, Syllabi, and Standards

In order to understand and use this part of the Instructor Module effectively, it is necessary to grasp three key concepts. Additional information can be found in the discussion of Knowledge Spaces theory (Chap. 8).

Item

An item is a fundamental unit of knowledge or ability recognized by the system. An example of an item in Basic Math is "Subtraction of Negative Integers." Every mathematical subject covered by **ALEKS** (such as Basic Math) corresponds to a set of items, each of which can be tested and taught by the system. Mastery of the subject means mastery of each of the items making up the subject.

Syllabus

A syllabus is a subset of the set of items belonging to a mathematical subject that has been defined as the goal for a particular course. For example, a syllabus for Basic Math is a set of items that students completing the course are expected to master. All assessment reports by the **ALEKS** system are based on some syllabus that has been selected by instructors or administrators for use by those students. The **ALEKS** Syllabus Editor is provided to permit instructors and administrators to customize existing syllabi (Sec. 6.4).

Standard

A standard is a set of syllabi, usually covering the entire range of levels over which a particular subject is taught. A standard should organize the teaching of a subject in a coherent and methodical way. That is, items belonging to the syllabus for one level should belong to the syllabi for higher levels, and items should be distributed among the syllabi according to some well-founded pedagogical rationale. A standard may be published by some social or governmental educational authority, or it may be created by a college or instructor for special purposes.

Under "Standards & Syllabi" users of the Instructor Module can navigate through a hierarchical listing of the standards currently available and the syllabus contained by them. Standards and syllabi can be copied. Users with appropriate levels of privilege can enter the Syllabus Editor to create new syllabi based on existing ones, possibly leading to the creation of new standards.

6.2 Navigation and Use

Access to directories under "Standards & Syllabi" is the same for all levels of user privilege, instructor and above. Any user of the Instructor Module may navigate through all directories and make copies of all available standards and syllabi. Users, however, may change only those standards and directories which they have themselves created (by copying existing ones), or those created by users within their authority. This means, for a root administrator, any administrator or instructor under their administration; for a college administrator, it means any instructor in the college. A user not within the authority of another given user has independent authority. Standards and syllabi created by a user with independent authority may not be changed. The privilege level of a particular user also determines where the new standards and syllabi created by that user will be placed.

- On choosing "Standards & Syllabi," the user begins with a master directory entitled "All Standards," containing a list of all the standards available for that system (Fig. 6.1).
- On opening any of the listed standards, the user is presented with a list of the levels covered by that standard.
- On opening any of the levels listed for the given standard, the user will see a list of the (mathematical) subjects covered for that level. At a minimum, there will be an element entitled "Basic." Each element in this list corresponds to a syllabus available within the system.

6.3   Buttons

The following buttons appear next to and beneath the navigation display in "Standards & Syllabi" (Fig. 6.1). The buttons are always visible; which buttons are active at any given moment depends on what is selected in the navigation display.

Edit Standard

The selected standard must have been created (copied from another standard) by the current user or by one within the authority of the current user. The basic standards included with **ALEKS** and syllabi created by users with independent authority cannot be changed, but they can be copied and the copies changed. A standard is defined by designating its name, source (authority), and an optional ID number. The "Enabled" button must be selected if the standard is intended for use.

Edit Syllabus

This will open the selected syllabus for modification in the Syllabus Editor (Sec. 6.4). The selected syllabus must have been created (copied from another syllabus) by the current user or by one within the authority of the current user. Syllabi belonging to the basic standards included with **ALEKS** and syllabi created by users with independent authority cannot be changed, but they can be copied and the copies changed.

Copy/new Standard

If a standard is selected, this will make a copy of that standard, usually for the purpose of establishing a new one based on it. If no standard is selected, it creates a new, empty one.

Copy/new Syllabus

If a syllabus is selected, this will make a copy of that syllabus, usually for the purpose of establishing a new one. If no syllabus is selected, it creates a new, empty one. If a new standard has been created, the new syllabus will be placed here.

6.4   Syllabus Editor

In order to make changes to syllabi that have been copied, users must select the new syllabus and click on the "Edit Syllabus" button (or double-click on the icon for that syllabus). This gives access to the **ALEKS** Syllabus Editor for that syllabus. Although the Syllabus Editor is always entered under the heading "Standards & Syllabi," it has its own, distinctive interface appearing beneath the "Standards & Syllabi" directory.

The Syllabus Editor displays items for the given subject, organized in folders by general topic. To see items you must open all folders in which they are contained.

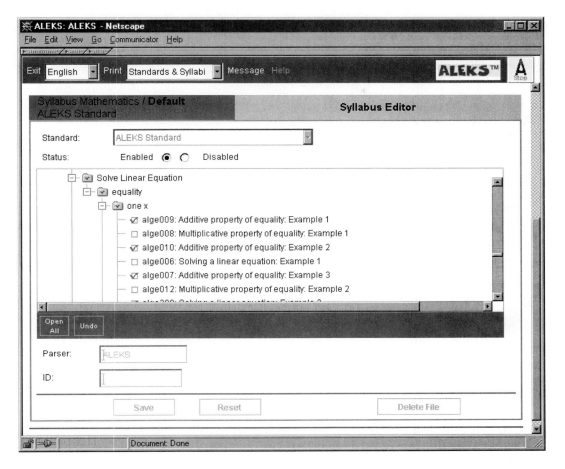

Figure 6.2: The Syllabus Editor (Instructor Module)

Items are labeled by name and topic, and indicate whether or not they belong to the current syllabus by a checkmark (Fig. 6.2). If a new syllabus is created by copying another syllabus, precisely the same items are selected in it as in the original. If the syllabus is created from scratch, no items in it are selected.

NOTE: If a folder is marked with a large checkmark, this means that all items in that folder currently belong to the syllabus. A small checkmark means that some of the items in that folder belong to the syllabus. No checkmark means no items in that folder belong to the syllabus.

Clicking on the tiny "x" in the upper right-hand corner of the directory window creates a single window and makes it possible to view all the items at once (click on "Open All").

6.4.1   Fields

The following fields appear above and below the editor display, and should be filled in as needed in creating or editing a syllabus.

Standard

> The standard to which this syllabus belongs.

Status

> Should be set to "enabled" if the syllabus is to be available for use.

Parser

> The name of the person creating or modifying the syllabus (and so responsible for its contents). To parse in this sense means to establish functional relationships between all elements of a sequence; the parser is making all items for the subject either members or nonmembers of the syllabus.

ID

> Optional identification number.

6.4.2   Buttons

The following buttons also appear adjacent to the editor display.

Open All

> Shows all folders in the editor display. This gives a complete picture of the topical structure of the subject matter.

Undo

> Undoes the most recent editing action (the addition or removal of an item).

6.4.3   Using the Syllabus Editor

To define a syllabus, the instructor must first ascertain which of the items in the complete list of items making up the subject matter are to belong to this syllabus. This should be a thoughtful decision, usually made within an appropriate institutional framework. Under normal circumstances, college courses in a mathematical subject include the entire list of items belonging to the subject, so that no editing of the syllabus delivered with **ALEKS** is needed. If a particular source is used for defining a syllabus, the source should be recorded in the standard containing the new syllabus, and should be documented externally as justification for the decision to adopt the given syllabus. If the course is part of a sequence, the syllabi for the other courses in this sequence will normally be defined together with it as part of a single progression.

Once the list of items to be included has been established, the instructor responsible for editing the syllabus examines each of the displayed items. There should be a checkmark before each item to be included, and no checkmark before items that are not to be included. A checkmark is added or removed by clicking once on the checkbox. Following this, click on the "Save" button to record the syllabus.

Chapter 7

Teaching with ALEKS

7.1 General

Certain recommendations concern the general framework within which **ALEKS** is used in college courses. Experience has shown that nothing is more important for successful use of **ALEKS** than making it a formal part of the course requirements. It should be included in the course syllabus, with a minimum number of hours required to be spent weekly on the system (we normally recommend three or more). Also, the initial assessment should be part of a general orientation to use of the system taking place under the instructor's supervision (Sec. 2.9). The facilities of the Instructor Module are directly relevant to putting these suggestions into practice.

7.2 Monitoring Student Use

In the day-to-day use of **ALEKS** by a class, a principal concern of the instructor is usually to monitor that students are using the system with the required regularity and for at least the minimum required amount of time. The most convenient place to find this information is the Progress page for a course (Sec. 5.5). Each student's name is displayed on this page with the total number of hours that student has spent logged on to the system.

7.3 Monitoring Course Progress

The instructor can also use the bar graphs to see how close each student is to mastery of the subject matter on the Course Progress page. It should be kept in mind that the bar graphs displayed on this page show only the students' achievement as of their last assessment (in blue) and any progress made in the Learning Mode since that assessment (in green). To see each of the assessments for a given student, with their progress subsequent to each assessment in the Learning Mode, the instructor should view the Student Progress page for that student. Do this either by selecting the student's name in the Results & Progress directory and clicking "Progress," or by clicking on the student's underlined name in the Course Progress display.

7.4   Monitoring Individual Progress

On the Student Progress page there is a line for each assessment taken by a particular student, with bar graphs showing mastery as of that assessment and subsequent progress made in the Learning Mode (Sec. 5.3). The initial assessment is shown in the bottom line, with later assessments "stacked" upward. By following progression from earlier to later assessments, the instructor can see very clearly how a student is progressing toward mastery of subject matter.

Some caution should be exercised in interpreting this information, however. Students vary widely both in the smoothness and in the speed with which they master material. It is seldom the case that progress made in the Learning Mode (green bar) is simply absorbed into a student's level of mastery on a subsequent assessment. Many students progress more quickly in assessment than in the Learning Mode. In such cases the "new" blue line is further ahead than the green line just below it. Other students make slower progress in assessment than in the Learning Mode. In such cases the "new" blue line lags behind the green line below it. It is very common for a student to master the entire subject matter two or more times in the Learning Mode before that mastery is finally confirmed in an assessment. None of these situations is cause for alarm. Part of the power of the **ALEKS** system is that it does not expect students to behave like machines and makes allowance for a robust and unpredictable "human factor."

NOTE: In cases where a student moves backward in their mastery, it may be worth the instructor's effort to make individual contact with the student. They may be experiencing a personal problem, there may have been help on an initial assessment, or there may be other external factors affecting the situation.

7.5   Moving a Student to a New Class

When a student completes the subject matter for a class whose syllabus corresponds to Basic Math, the instructor should unenroll that student from Basic Math in **ALEKS**, and reenroll the student in a new class whose syllabus corresponds to Algebra (Sec. 5.17). If no such class exists, it should be created so that the student is not prevented from making further progress.

It is possible to define classes in such a way that they include all subjects that the students are likely to begin learning before the end of the course (e.g., Basic Math & Algebra). This has the advantage that no students need to be moved from one **ALEKS** "class" to another. On the other hand, the experience of completing a domain and being "graduated" to another one is rewarding for the student. We recommend maximizing the opportunities for highlighting achievement in this way.

7.6   Ordering Assessments

Following the initial assessment (which should be taken under the instructor's supervision), the **ALEKS** system will automatically schedule any other assessments needed for correctly informing and guiding a student's progress. It is, however, a good practice for the instructor to schedule supervised assessments at regular intervals (midterm and end of the course), in order to have reliable information on the overall effectiveness of **ALEKS** with that course (Secs. 5.7–5.8).

7.7   Focused Instruction

Using the Student Report page, the instructor can determine precisely where the greatest gaps in the knowledge of an individual student exist and provide special assistance to students on this basis (to the extent that time and resources allow). Similarly, the Course Report page can be used to define priorities for instruction of entire groups (Sec. 5.6). If this page shows that 95 percent of the students in a group have mastered square roots, it is clear that the instructor does not need to spend time on this topic with the entire class. An instructor may choose to group students according to mastery levels, mixing (or not) students with varying levels of mastery of particular concepts.

The Course Report page can also be used to coach small groups within a larger course on topics that they are working on in the Learning Mode or will be soon. By choosing the "Ready to learn" display mode in the Course Report, the instructor can obtain a list of concepts that students in the course are most "ready to learn" with the names of students ready to learn them (Sec. 5.6). This information makes it possible to organize the course into a small groups on an *ad hoc* basis to work with students on topics they are currently being offered within the system. A whole new kind of flexible "threading" and "rethreading" of math instruction becomes thoroughly practical.

The informed use of Instructor Module features allows **ALEKS** to optimize student progress not only at the individual level, but also by guiding the work of small groups and of the entire course.

7.8   Independent Study and Distance Learning

The **ALEKS** system is well suited to use in an independent study or distance learning context. **ALEKS** is self-contained and adaptable to any syllabus or course materials. A student using **ALEKS** under these circumstances knows exactly what the course goals are, where they stand in relation to those goals, and where to find the instructional and practice tools to achieve them.

For the instructor administering an independent study or distance learning program, **ALEKS** solves every imaginable problem of management, oversight, evaluation, and communication. All of the information needed to keep track of far-flung independent learners is at the instructor's fingertips, through the features of the Instructor Module. The internal message system of **ALEKS** puts the instructor in constant touch with students without dependence on the vagaries of telephone or even email communication.

Chapter 8

Knowledge Spaces and the Theory Behind ALEKS

8.1 History

Knowledge Space theory has been under development since 1983 by Professor Jean-Claude Falmagne, who is the Chairman and founder of ALEKS Corporation, and other scientists (especially, Jean-Paul Doignon from Belgium) in the United States and Europe.

ALEKS is the first computer system to embody Knowledge Space theory for the assessment and teaching of an academic discipline.

8.2 Theory

An exposition of Knowledge Space theory is not intended here, nor is one necessary for the purposes of this manual. Knowledge Space theory is expressed in a mathematical discipline often referred to as "Combinatorics." The Bibliography contains a number of references for those interested in further details (Sec. 8.3). What follows here is a brief, intuitive summary introducing certain fundamental terms employed in discussions of **ALEKS**.

8.2.1 Domain, Items, and Instances

An academic discipline such as Basic Math or Algebra is represented as a particular set of problems or questions that comprehensively embody the knowledge of the discipline. That set is called the *domain*, and the problems are called *items*. Figure 8.1 gives a symbolic representation of the domain of Basic Math, with dots standing for

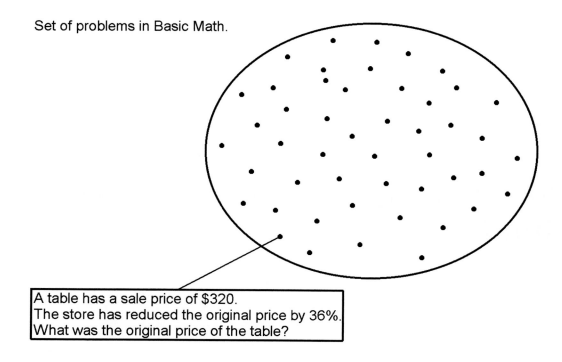

Set of problems in Basic Math.

A table has a sale price of $320.
The store has reduced the original price by 36%.
What was the original price of the table?

Figure 8.1: Domain of Basic Math

items. One of the items, which might be entitled "Word Problem with Percentages," is indicated by a line. The problem in the rectangle is an *instance* of that item.

Each item, or problem-type, has dozens, sometimes hundreds, of instances. In **ALEKS**, the domain of Basic Math is made up of about one hundred items, ranging from two-digit addition (without carry), to negative exponents. Algebra has a domain containing around two hundred items. Full mastery of the domain implies the ability to solve problems corresponding to all the items making up the domain.

Determining the set of items that make up the domain is the first step in constructing a "knowledge structure" for that domain. This is done by research in instructional materials and standards and very systematic, painstaking consultation with instructors. Substantial agreement is achieved among expert pedagogues on the choice and definition of items. The set of items finally arrived at and forming the domain must be comprehensive, that is, it must cover all the concepts that are essential in the particular academic discipline.

8.2.2   Knowledge States

The *knowledge state* of a student is represented by the set of items in the domain that he or she is capable of solving under ideal conditions (Fig. 8.2). This means

A possible knowledge state.
In Basic Math, we use a knowledge structure
with roughly 40,000 states.

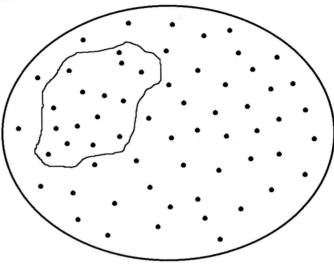

Figure 8.2: Knowledge State

that the student is not working under time pressure, is not impaired by emotional turmoil of any kind, etc. In reality, careless errors may arise. Also, the correct response to a question may occasionally be guessed by a subject lacking any real understanding of the question asked. (This will occur very rarely when using the **ALEKS** system, because multiple-choice answers are not used.) In general, an individual's knowledge state is thus not directly observable, and has to be inferred from the responses to the questions.

8.2.3 Knowledge Structures and Knowledge Spaces

It should be intuitively obvious that not all possible subsets of the domain are feasible knowledge states. For instance, every student having mastered "long division" would also have mastered "addition of decimal numbers." Thus, there is no knowledge state containing the "long division" item that does not also contain the "addition of decimal numbers" item. The collection of all feasible knowledge states is referred to as the *knowledge structure*. In the current implementation of **ALEKS** for Basic Math, the number of feasible knowledge states is approximately 40,000. Thus, the knowledge structure for Basic Math contains approximately 40,000 knowledge states. In order to assess a student in Basic Math, **ALEKS** must find out by efficient questioning which of these 40,000 states the student is in. This large number of

The beginning of a possible learning path.
Our structure in Basic Math allows for
billions of them.

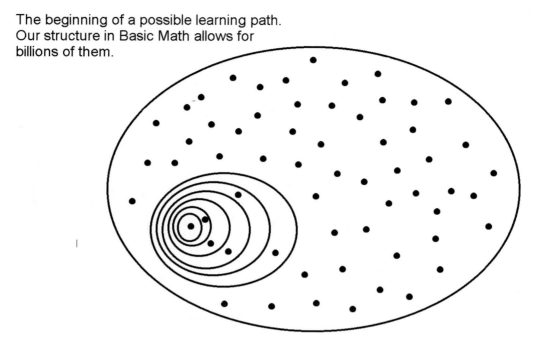

Figure 8.3: Learning Path

states means that there are many possible ways of acquiring knowledge, i.e., many learning paths (Fig. 8.3). In the knowledge structure of **ALEKS** for Basic Math, there are literally billions of such learning paths. A "knowledge space" is a particular kind of knowledge structure.

As in many real-life applications, "noise" and errors of various sorts often creep in, which require the elaboration of a probabilistic theory. The **ALEKS** System is based on such a probabilistic theory, which makes it capable of recovering elegantly from any misconceptions. For instance, **ALEKS** is capable of deciding that a student has mastered an item, even though the student has actually made an error when presented with a problem instantiating this item. This is not mysterious: a sensible examiner in an oral exam, observing an error to a question about addition would nevertheless conclude that the student has mastered addition, for example, if that student had given evidence of skillful manipulation of exponents.

8.2.4   Inner and Outer Fringes of a Knowledge State

An item that has not yet been mastered by a student may not be immediately learnable by that student. Learning one or more prerequisite items may be necessary. Consider a student in a particular knowledge state K. The set of all items that may be learned immediately by a student in that state K is called the *outer fringe* of the

A knowledge state and its outer fringe.

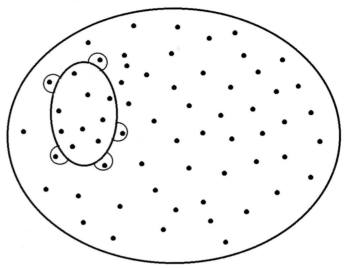

Figure 8.4: Outer Fringe of a Knowledge State

state K. More precisely, an item is in the outer fringe of the state K if the addition of that item to the state K forms a new, feasible knowledge state (Fig. 8.4). Typically, the outer fringe of a knowledge state will contain between one and a few items.

Similarly, an item is in the inner fringe of a state K if there is some other knowledge state to which that item may be added to form state K (Fig. 8.5). The *inner fringe* of a state K is thus defined as the set of all items which **may** have been the last one learned.

These two concepts of inner and outer fringes are used in powerful ways in the learning mode of the **ALEKS** System. For example, the system always offers a student problems to solve that are based on items in the outer fringe of his or her state. If **ALEKS** judges that a student is experiencing difficulties in learning some new item, **ALEKS** typically reviews the mastery of items in the inner fringe of the student's state that are also related to the new item to be learned.

8.2.5 Assessment

How can **ALEKS** uncover, by efficient questioning, the particular knowledge state of a student? While the details of **ALEKS**'s method for achieving such a goal are technical, the guiding intuition is commonsensical. At every moment of an assessment, **ALEKS** chooses a question to be "as informative as possible." In our context, this means a question which the student has, in the system's estimate,

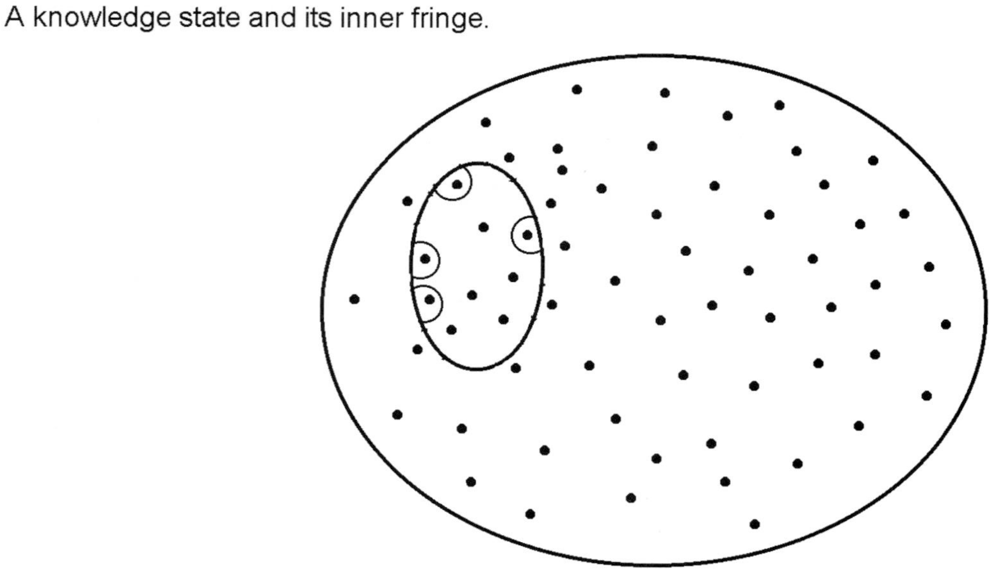

A knowledge state and its inner fringe.

Figure 8.5: Inner Fringe of a Knowledge State

about a 50 percent chance of getting right. The student's response (correct or false) determines a change in all the likelihood values: for instance, if the question involved a manipulation of fractions, and the student's response was correct, then all the knowledge states containing this item would have their likelihood values increased. The specific way the questions are chosen and the likelihood values altered makes it possible for **ALEKS** to pinpoint the student's state quite accurately in a relatively short time. In Basic Math, for example, approximately 15–20 questions often suffice.

Finally, it should be noted that the assessment report given to students, instructors, and administrators is a very precise *summary* of the student's knowledge state. If the structure is known, the outer fringe and inner fringe together completely define the student's knowledge state. Internally, the system registers the student's knowledge or non-knowledge of each item in the domain.

A comprehensive treatment of Knowledge Spaces theory can be found in Doignon & Falmagne, *Knowledge Spaces* (Springer-Verlag, 1999).

8.3   Select Bibliography

Degreef, E., Doignon J.-P., Ducamp A., & Falmagne J.-C. (1986). Languages for the assessment of knowledge. *Journal of Mathematical Psychology, 30,* 243-256.

Doignon, J.-P. & Falmagne, J.-C. (1985). Spaces for the assessment of knowledge. *International Journal of Man-Machine Studies, 23*, 175-196.

Doignon, J.-P. & Falmagne, J.-C. (1999) *Knowledge Spaces.* Springer-Verlag.

Dowling, C.E. (1993). Applying the basis of knowledge space for controlling the questioning of an expert. *Journal of Mathematical Psychology, 37*, 21-48.

Dowling, C.E. (1993). On the irredundant construction of knowledge spaces. *Journal of Mathematical Psychology, 37*, 49-62.

Falmagne, J.-C. (1989). A latent trait theory via stochastic learning theory for a knowledge space. *Psychometrika, 54*, 283-303.

Falmagne, J.-C. & Doignon, J.-P. (1988). A class of stochastic procedures for the assessment of knowledge. *British Journal of Mathematical and Statistical Psychology, 41*, 1-23.

Falmagne, J.-C. & Doignon, J.-P. (1988). A markovian procedure for assessing the state of a system. *Journal of Mathematical Psychology, 32*, 232-258.

Falmagne, J.-C., Koppen, M., Villano, M., Doignon, J.-P. & Johannesen, L. (1990). Introduction to knowledge spaces: How to build test and search them. *Psychological Review, 97*, 201-224.

Kambouri, M., Koppen, M., Villano, M. & Falmagne, J.-C. (1991). Knowledge assessment: Tapping human expertise. *Irvine Research Unit in Mathematical Behavioral Sciences. University of California.*

Koppen, M. (1993). Extracting human expertise for constructing knowledge spaces: An algorithm. *Journal of Mathematical Psychology, 37*, 1-20.

Koppen, M. & Doignon, J.-P. (1990). How to build a knowledge space by querying an expert. *Journal of Mathematical Psychology, 34*, 311-331.

Villano, M., Falmagne, J.-C., Johannesen, L. & Doignon, J.-P. Stochastic procedures for assessing an individual's state of knowledge. *In: Proceedings of the int. conf. on computer assisted learning in post-secondary educ.*

Chapter 9

Frequently Asked Questions

9.1 General

What is ALEKS?

ALEKS is the new way to learn math on the World Wide Web. By knowing exactly which math concepts the student has mastered, which are shaky, and which are new but within reach, **ALEKS** enables the student to work on those concepts the student is most ready to learn. **ALEKS** is a full-time automated tutor, including explanations, practice and feedback. **ALEKS** closely interacts with the student, continuously updating its precise map of the student's knowledge state. **ALEKS** combines the advantages of one-on-one instruction and evaluation with the convenience of being on-call, on your computer, 24 hours a day, seven days a week. The cost of **ALEKS** is a small fraction of the cost of a human tutor.

What makes ALEKS different?

A great many important differences exist between **ALEKS** and other kinds of "educational software," including its finely individualized instructional features, easy access over the World Wide Web, its rigorous and comprehensive educational content, and its course-management module for instructors and administrators. A critical difference is the capacity of **ALEKS** for efficient, precise, comprehensive, and qualitative assessment. This not only makes it a valuable tool for monitoring educational progress, but also enables it to provide students with the material they are most able to learn at a particular time. This means that the students are given neither material that they have already mastered nor material that they are not well suited to work on yet because some prerequisites have yet to be learned.

ALEKS is a self-contained learning environment, with complete sets of practice and explanatory units needed for the subjects that it covers. The units may also be referenced or linked to textbooks for extended treatment of mathematical concepts. There is an online student mathematics dictionary accessed by clicking on underlined mathematical terms (hypertext links), and a diagnostic feedback facility that, in many cases, is able to explain the nature of misunderstandings and errors made by students.

For instructors, **ALEKS** offers a complete administrative and monitoring facility through which individual and group progress can be checked, standards can be established, enrollment managed, and messages exchanged. **ALEKS** can be configured for use with diverse educational standards.

ALEKS is not a game or "edutainment." It is an automated educational tool with robust, carefully-designed features for both learners and educators.

What are the parts or "modules" of ALEKS?

The principal "modules" of **ALEKS** are the *Assessment Module*, in which student knowledge is rigorously assessed, the *Learning Module*, where students work on mastering specific concepts, the *Instructor Module*, in which instructors and administrators are able to monitor student progress and carry out administrative functions, and the *Administrator Module*, which permits management and monitoring of an arbitrary number of separate institutions, such as those making up a State or County college system. There is also a Tutorial (which students take once when first registering with the system), online help, a mathematics Dictionary, graphic display of assessment results and learning progress, and many other features.

Why is ALEKS on the Internet?

ALEKS is available on the Internet so that a student who has registered with the system can use it from any suitable computer, in an educational institution, at home, or anywhere else. Very little technical preparation must be done to use the system. All you need is a self-installing, self-maintaining "plugin" obtained directly from the **ALEKS** website for Higher Education. No disks, CD's, peripherals, or backup facilities are required. All data is kept on the ALEKS Corporation server.

9.2 Technical

What are the technical requirements for using ALEKS?

[**Sec. 2.2**] The following table presents the technical requirements for **ALEKS** in summary form:

	PC	Macintosh
Operating System	Windows 95/98/NT4.0 or higher	MacOS 7.6.1 or higher
Processor	Pentium 133+ MHz (166+ preferred), Pentium II/III	
RAM Memory	32+ MB	32+ MB
Browser	Netscape 4.5 or higher, Explorer 4.0 or higher	Netscape 4.5 or higher
Modem Speed	28+ kbps	28+ kbps

Note that any of the kinds of direct connection (cable, ISDN, DSL) that are typical in computer labs are adequate for use with **ALEKS**. If your computer lab has security safeguards in place, you will need the cooperation of your LAN administrator, system administrator, or lab technician to install the **ALEKS** plugin.

NOTE: Netscape Communicator 4.0x (4.01, 4.02, etc.) is not compatible with **ALEKS** and should be upgraded to 4.5 or later. This can be done from the Netscape website:

http://www.netscape.com

If you have America Online 3.0 you will have to upgrade to America Online 4.0 or higher in order to use **ALEKS**. You can upgrade from AOL.

Where can I get more information on ALEKS? How can I try out the system?

The **ALEKS** website for Higher Education provides complete information on the **ALEKS** system, including a Quick Tour, Guest registration, licensing, history and theory, and technical support.

http://www.highed.aleks.com

9.3 Theory

What is the theory behind ALEKS?

[**Chap. 8**] [**Sec. 8.3**] **ALEKS** is based on a field of Cognitive Science (Mathematical Psychology) called "Knowledge Spaces." The purpose of research in Knowledge Spaces is to model human knowledge in any subject, using mathematical tools such as Set Theory, Combinatorics, and Markovian Processes, so as to make possible fast and accurate assessment through interactive computer applications. There are numerous scientific publications in the field of Knowledge Spaces dating back to the early 1980's. A recent, authoritative treatment (with Bibliography) is Doignon & Falmagne, *Knowledge Spaces* (Springer-Verlag, 1999).

What is an "item"?

[**Sec. 8.2.1**] In Knowledge Space theory, an "item" is a concept or skill to be learned, the mastery of which is captured by a "problem-type" serving as the basis for specific assessment and practice problems. Thus the item "addition of two-digit numbers without carry" might produce the problem (instance) "What is 25 plus 11?"

What is a "domain"?

[**Sec. 8.2.1**] In Knowledge Space theory, a "domain" is the set of all items making up a particular subject matter, such as Basic Math. A learner is considered to have mastered the domain when that learner can solve problems corresponding to all the items in the domain.

What is a "knowledge state"?

[**Sec. 8.2.2**] In Knowledge Space theory, a "knowledge state" is the set of items belonging to a domain that a learner has mastered at some point in time. We speak of knowledge states in relation to a particular learner and a particular domain. Obviously, a learner's knowledge state changes in time, and the goal of learning is that it should eventually include (correspond to) the entire domain.

What is the "outer fringe" of a knowledge state?

[**Sec. 8.2.4**] In Knowledge Space theory, a learner's "outer fringe" is the set of items, any one of which can be added to the current knowledge state, to make a new, feasible knowledge state. These are the items that the student is considered most "ready to learn."

Progress is made from one state to another through one of the items in the first state's "outer fringe."

What is the "inner fringe" of a knowledge state?

[**Sec. 8.2.4**] In Knowledge Space theory, a learner's "inner fringe" is the set of items, any one of which can be taken away from the current knowledge state, to make a new, feasible knowledge state. These are the items that the student may have learned recently, and thus whose knowledge might be shaky.

What is a "knowledge structure"? What is a "knowledge space"?

[**Sec. 8.2.3**] In Knowledge Space theory, "knowledge structure" or "knowledge space" (the two concepts differ in a technical way) refers to the collection of feasible knowledge states for a particular domain. It is a key point that not all sets of items from the domain (subsets of the domain) are feasible knowledge states. For instance, there can be no knowledge state containing the item "finding the square root of an integer" that does not contain the item "addition of two-digit numbers without carry," since no one will master the first without having mastered the second.

How was the structure created?

The knowledge structures (or, briefly, "structures") used by **ALEKS** are created by analysis of the subject matter and extensive, computer-aided querying of expert instructors. When **ALEKS** assesses a student, it is actually searching the structure for knowledge states that match the student's present competence.

What is the educational philosophy behind ALEKS?

The educational use of **ALEKS** is not tied to any particular theory of education or knowledge acquisition. A key insight underlying **ALEKS** is the existence of a vast multiplicity of diverse "learning paths" or sequences of topics by which a field can be mastered. Based on an inventory of knowledge states that numbers in the tens of thousands (for the subjects currently covered by **ALEKS**), the specialized mathematical tools of Knowledge Space theory make it possible for the system to accommodate literally billions of possible individual learning paths implied by the relations among states.

ALEKS does not embody a particular philosophy of teaching mathematics; rather, it is compatible with any pedagogical approach.

9.4 Assessments & Reports

What is an ALEKS assessment?

[**Chap. 3**] An assessment by the **ALEKS** system consists of a sequence of mathematical problems posed to the student. The answers are in the form of mathematical expressions and constructions produced by the system's input tools (no multiple-choice). The student is encouraged to answer "I don't know" where this is appropriate. During an **ALEKS** assessment, the student is not told whether answers are correct or incorrect. The assessment is adaptive. Each question after the first is chosen on the basis of answers previously submitted. Assessment problems (like practice problems) are algorithmically generated with random numerical values. The length of the assessment is variable, between 15 and 35 questions. There are no time constraints, but most assessments can take less than a half-hour and rarely more than an hour. Students taking an assessment need to have paper and pencil. Calculators are not permitted in assessments for Basic Math, but simple calculators (without graphing or symbolic functions) are permitted for Algebra. A basic calculator is part of **ALEKS**. No help whatsoever should be given to students taking an assessment, not even rephrasing problems. Outside help can easily lead to false assessment results and hinder subsequent work in the **ALEKS** Learning Mode.

Students are always assessed when they first register with the **ALEKS** system. It is highly advisable that all assessments from which the instructor uses data in any way (such as for placement) take place under the instructor's supervision. At a minimum, the initial assessment must be supervised.

How does the ALEKS assessment work?

[**Sec. 8.2.5**] In assessing a student's knowledge, the system is in fact determining which of the feasible knowledge states for that subject corresponds to the student's current knowledge. The assessment is probabilistic, so that it is not fooled by careless errors. (Lucky guesses are very rare, because multiple-choice answers are not used.) At the beginning of the assessment, students are asked to roughly estimate their knowledge of the subject matter. With some account taken of this estimate, likelihood values (values for the likelihood that the student is in a particular knowledge state) are spread out over the states belonging to the structure. With each correct answer, the likelihood of states containing the item for which a correct answer was given is raised and that of states not containing the item lowered. The reverse occurs for incorrect answers or "I don't know." At each step of the assessment, the system attempts to choose an item for which it estimates (based on current likelihood values) the student has about a fifty-fifty chance of success; such questions are maximally informative. When the likelihood values of a few states are extremely high and those of all the rest are extremely low (in technical terms, when the entropy of the structure is lower than a certain threshold value), the assessment ends and results are produced.

If a student makes a careless error or lucky guess, this will appear inconsistent with the general tendency of the student's responses and the system will "probe" that area of knowledge until it is sure. For this reason, inconsistent assessments (often resulting from lack of concentration) may require more questions.

How should I interpret the assessment report?

[**Sec. 3.6**] The results of an **ALEKS** assessment are shown in the form of one or more piecharts. A piechart corresponds to a subject matter (domain) or to the curriculum of a particular course. Each slice of the pie corresponds to a general topic. The degree to which the slice is filled in with solid color shows how close the student is to mastering that area. Where courses are being taken in sequence, there may be piecharts showing the previous and/or subsequent courses in that sequence. (Experience shows that in such cases learning goes on at different curricular levels simultaneously, so multiple charts are indispensable.)

An extremely important aspect of the piecharts is their indication of what a student is currently most "ready to learn" (that is, the "outer fringe" of the student's current knowledge state). These items are listed beneath the piecharts in an Assessment Report and are also given through the piecharts themselves. When the mouse pointer is placed over a slice of the pie, a list pops out showing the concepts that the student is most "ready to learn" in that part of the curriculum (there may be none). Clicking on any of these concepts takes the student into the Learning Mode to work on it.

The piecharts are displayed following assessments, after a concept has been worked on in the Learning Mode, and when a student clicks on "MyPie" to change topics. At any given time, a student can only choose to work on concepts that the student is currently most "ready to learn." This number may vary between two and a dozen, depending on what part of the structure is involved.

9.5 Learning Mode

What is the Learning Mode?

[**Chap. 4**] The Learning Mode in **ALEKS** contains features to help students practice and master specific mathematical concepts and skills. In the Learning Mode, students are always working on a specific concept that they have chosen and that, in the system's estimation, they are fully prepared to master. If the learner successfully solves an appropriate number of problems based on that concept, the system will tentatively determine that it has been mastered and offer a new choice of topics. If the student has difficulty, the system will attempt to diagnose the student's errors. It will also provide explanations of how to solve problems and definitions of mathematical terms. It may suggest the name of a classmate who can help. If the student is unable to master the concept right now, or if the student wishes to change topics, a new choice of topics will be offered. After a certain time has been spent in the Learning Mode, or after a certain amount of progress has been made, the student will be reassessed automatically unless the instructor has already requested a new assessment.

What is the relationship between the Assessment Mode and the Learning Mode in ALEKS?

The Assessment and Learning Modes work together in a cyclical fashion, beginning with the initial assessment. A student is assessed, and the results of the assessment serve as a basis for the student's entry into the Learning Mode (the student works on concepts that the assessment showed that student most "ready to learn"). After a certain time in the Learning Mode, during which the results of the previous assessment are tentatively updated according to whether the student masters or fails to master new concepts, the student is reassessed and the cycle begins again. In this sense, **ALEKS** is an interactive learning system guided and powered by ongoing diagnostic assessment.

9.6 Educational Use

What is the best way to use ALEKS with my course?

The greatest factor in successful use of **ALEKS** is regular, structured use, with close monitoring of student progress by the instructor. We recommend scheduling regular lab sessions with **ALEKS**, totalling a minimum of three hours per week, as part of your course requirements. Not every lab session need be supervised by the instructor, but the initial assessment certainly should be. Any other interim and concluding assessments scheduled specially by the instructor normally should also be supervised.

This having been said, there has been successful use of **ALEKS** in a very wide variety of contexts and structures, including independent study. ALEKS Corporation is happy to consult with instructors on the best way to use **ALEKS** with their students.

Can ALEKS be used with handicapped and learning-disability students? Is ALEKS a remedial tool?

ALEKS is designed to help all students who can read sufficiently to understand what it says, and who can use a computer. It has been used successfully with students exhibiting a range of learning disabilities. Students with reading difficulties can also use it, provided that there is someone on hand to help them as needed. The system does not currently contain facilities for audio output.

What burden will ALEKS place on our computer lab and Lab Director/LAN Administrator?

Normally **ALEKS** requires very little support from local computer technicians, given the automatic installation and maintenance of the **ALEKS** plugin. Most of the time, however, the lab administrator will need to assist with installation in order to overcome security obstacles (for excellent reasons, college computer labs tend to prevent students from installing their own software). In a few cases, the

presence of a "firewall" or other security measures may require some work on the
technician's part for successful installation. Again, ALEKS Corporation stands
ready to assist with problems of this nature.

Does ALEKS need to be used with a particular textbook?

ALEKS is designed to be used with any syllabus, curriculum, or textbook. The
system may also be referenced or linked to a textbook or online applications for
particular courses. The fundamental idea of the **ALEKS** system is to allow students to pursue individualized paths to mastery of the subject matter. For this
reason instructors may very commonly find their students learning material that
has not yet been covered in the course. This should be regarded as a sign of the
system's effective use.

Does ALEKS have special features for educators?

[**Chaps. 5–6**] Students' use of **ALEKS** and their progress toward mastery can
be monitored using the facilities of the Instructor Module. The Instructor Module
(called Administrator Module when it includes more than one institution) also
enables instructors and administrators to establish the syllabi and standards used
by **ALEKS**, to configure accounts, to find statistics on institutional use, and to
exchange messages. An instructor or administrator who has been registered with
ALEKS enters the Instructor Module immediately upon login.

What are Results & Progress? What are Standards & Syllabi?

There are two parts of the Instructor Module, "Results & Progress" and "Standards
& Syllabi." The former is by far the more commonly used. It contains information on system use and progress by students and groups, as well as all necessary
facilities for account and database management. The latter is used strategically,
to define the standards and syllabi that will be used over extended periods of time
by colleges. Actions taken in "Standards & Syllabi" should be the outcome of
well-considered institutional decisions.

How does ALEKS define standards and syllabi?

[**Chap. 6**] In **ALEKS**, a "syllabus" is the set of items belonging to a domain that is
determined to be the goal for mastery in a particular course. In a typical situation,
the syllabus of a college Basic Math course will be the entire set of items for Basic
Math. If the syllabus does not contain the entire domain, it is defined by selection
of a particular subset of the domain. This is done in the Syllabus editor by adding
and removing checkmarks next to the names of items. A "Standard" in **ALEKS**
is a group of syllabi considered to constitute a logical, integrated sequence.

How can I use ALEKS Educational Support?

[**Sec. 10.1**] You can contact ALEKS Corporation using the information in Chapter 10 of this manual. We request that this information not be given to students.
ALEKS Corporation does not provide technical or other support directly to students using **ALEKS** in college courses. Students should approach their instructor
first with any questions or problems regarding the use of **ALEKS**. Questions the
instructor is unable to answer can then be brought to our attention.

Chapter 10

Support

10.1 Support

NOTE: Troubleshooting information is found in Appendix A of this manual (Sec. A.10). Most problems can be resolved using this brief reference.

Current information on **ALEKS** is available at the ALEKS website for Higher Education:

> **http://www.highed.aleks.com**

Technical support and consultation on the effective use of **ALEKS** is provided to educators by ALEKS Corporation. Please contact us by email:

> **highed-support@aleks.com**

by telephone:

> **(949) 253-8220**

or by fax:

> **(949) 253-8228**

In reporting problems and seeking support, please make a xerox copy of the form provided and gather complete information as a preliminary to contacting us (Sec. 10.2). This will help us to resolve any difficulties as quickly and completely as possible. Instructors should have their students fill out these forms for problems that occur in accessing **ALEKS** from home. In many cases the information provided by students should enable instructors to resolve the problems themselves. If this is not possible, the instructor should contact ALEKS Corporation with all relevant information.

NOTE: We ask that students using **ALEKS** not contact us directly, but approach their instructors first. It is hoped that the information in this *Instructor's Manual* will enable instructors to answer many of their students' questions.

We also welcome any and all comments and feedback on **ALEKS**. Here is our mailing address:

ALEKS Corporation
Higher Education Customer Support
17742B Mitchell North
Irvine, CA 92614

10.2 Form for Reporting Problems

Please use the following form to gather information before reporting a problem: (Make a copy to avoid writing in the book.)

ALEKS Corporation FAX (949) 253-8228

<u>**USER**</u>   (Higher Education)

Name: _____ Telephone: _____ Email: _____
College: _____ Instructor: _____ Course: _____
Best time to call: _____

<u>**COMPUTER ON WHICH PROBLEM OCCURRED**</u> (Sec. A.2)

Computer make and model name or number: _____
Processor type and speed (MHz): _____ RAM (MB): _____

Connection:	Modem ☐	Speed: _____
	Cable ☐ DSL ☐ ISDN ☐ Other: _____ ☐
Browser:	Netscape	4.5 ☐ 4.6 ☐ 4.7 ☐ _____ ☐
	Internet Explorer	4._____ ☐ 5._____ ☐ _____ ☐
	AOL	4._____ ☐ 5._____ ☐ _____ ☐
	Other: _____
Operating System:	Windows	95 ☐ 98 ☐ _____ ☐
	Windows NT	4.0 ☐ _____ ☐
	MacOS	7._____ ☐ 8._____ ☐ _____ ☐
	Other: _____

<u>**WHERE PROBLEM OCCURRED**</u>   (Sec. A.10)

(URL used to access **ALEKS**: _____)
1. going to the **ALEKS** website   (Sec. A.3) ☐
2. installing the plugin   (Secs. A.3,A.7) ☐
3. logging on to **ALEKS**   (Secs. A.3,A.6) ☐
4. using **ALEKS** in:

                Registration (Sec. A.3) ☐ Tutorial (Sec. A.4) ☐
                Assessment (Sec. A.5.1) ☐ Report (Sec. A.5.2) ☐
                Learning Mode (Sec. A.5.3) ☐

<u>**PRECISE ERROR MESSAGE (if any):**</u>

<u>**DESCRIPTION OF PROBLEM:**</u>   (Recurrent? Yes ☐ No ☐)

My technical proficiency: Beginner ☐ Intermediate ☐ High ☐

Appendix A

ALEKS User's Guide

A.1   Preface

Welcome to **ALEKS**! You are about to discover one of the most powerful educational tools available for college mathematics. Combining advanced learning technology with the flexibility of the World Wide Web, the **ALEKS** system provides a "smart" interactive tutoring system with unmatched features and capabilities. Richly supplied with illustrations and reference materials, **ALEKS** constantly challenges you and supplies extensive feedback on what you have accomplished. **ALEKS** will always help you select the ideal topic to work on now. That way you learn concepts in the order that's best for you. **ALEKS** provides individualized, one-on-one instruction that fits your schedule. It is available wherever you access the Web.

ALEKS was developed with support from the National Science Foundation. It is based on a field of Mathematical Cognitive Science called "Knowledge Spaces." The purpose of research in Knowledge Spaces is to model human knowledge of any subject for quick and precise assessment by interactive computer programs.

The **ALEKS** system is self-explanatory and includes online instructions and feedback. This booklet contains basic information to help students begin using **ALEKS**. Instructors using **ALEKS** with their courses are provided with an *Instructor's Manual* containing complete information on the system's operation. They should be able to answer any questions beyond those dealt with in these pages.

NOTE: ALEKS is designed for use without help from a manual. Your instructor will assist you in registering with the system and beginning to use it. If questions arise, or if you want to learn more about ALEKS, use this *Guide*. It is intended as a convenient and concise reference.

Only registered users can keep an account on ALEKS. (Anyone may try the system as a guest.) Two or more persons cannot use the same

ALEKS account. The system will regard them as a single person and give incorrect guidance.

A.2   Technical Requirements

PC Requirements

You can use **ALEKS** on any PC with a Pentium processor of 133 MHz or more (166+ MHz preferred) or any Pentium II or Pentium III processor. At least 32 MB of RAM are required. Your operating system must be Windows 95/98/NT4.0 or higher.

The following popular web browsers are compatible with **ALEKS** on PCs: Netscape Communicator 4.5 or higher, Internet Explorer 4.0 or higher.

Macintosh Requirements

ALEKS can be used on a Macintosh, iMac, or Macintosh G3-G4 with at least 32 MB of RAM. Your operating system must be MacOS 7.6.1 or higher.

Only Netscape Communicator 4.5 and higher is supported for the Macintosh.

Note

Netscape Communicator 4.0x (4.01, 4.02, etc.) is not compatible with **ALEKS** and should be upgraded to 4.5 or higher. This can be done from the Netscape website:

http://www.netscape.com

Internet Access

ALEKS is used over the World Wide Web. You must have an Internet connection by dialup modem (at least 28k) or any other kind of access to the Internet (cable, ISDN, DSL, etc.).

America Online Subscribers

If you have America Online 3.0 you will have to upgrade to America Online 4.0 or higher in order to use **ALEKS**. You can upgrade from AOL.

A.3   Registration & Installation

Before You Begin: In order to register as an **ALEKS** user you need the **Access Code** inside the back cover of this booklet. You also need a **Course Code** provided by your instructor. When you register with the **ALEKS** system your name is entered into the database and records of your progress are kept. If the **ALEKS** plugin has not been installed on the computer being used for registration, it will be installed automatically as part of this procedure.

Step 1: Go to the **ALEKS** website for Higher Education by typing in the following address:

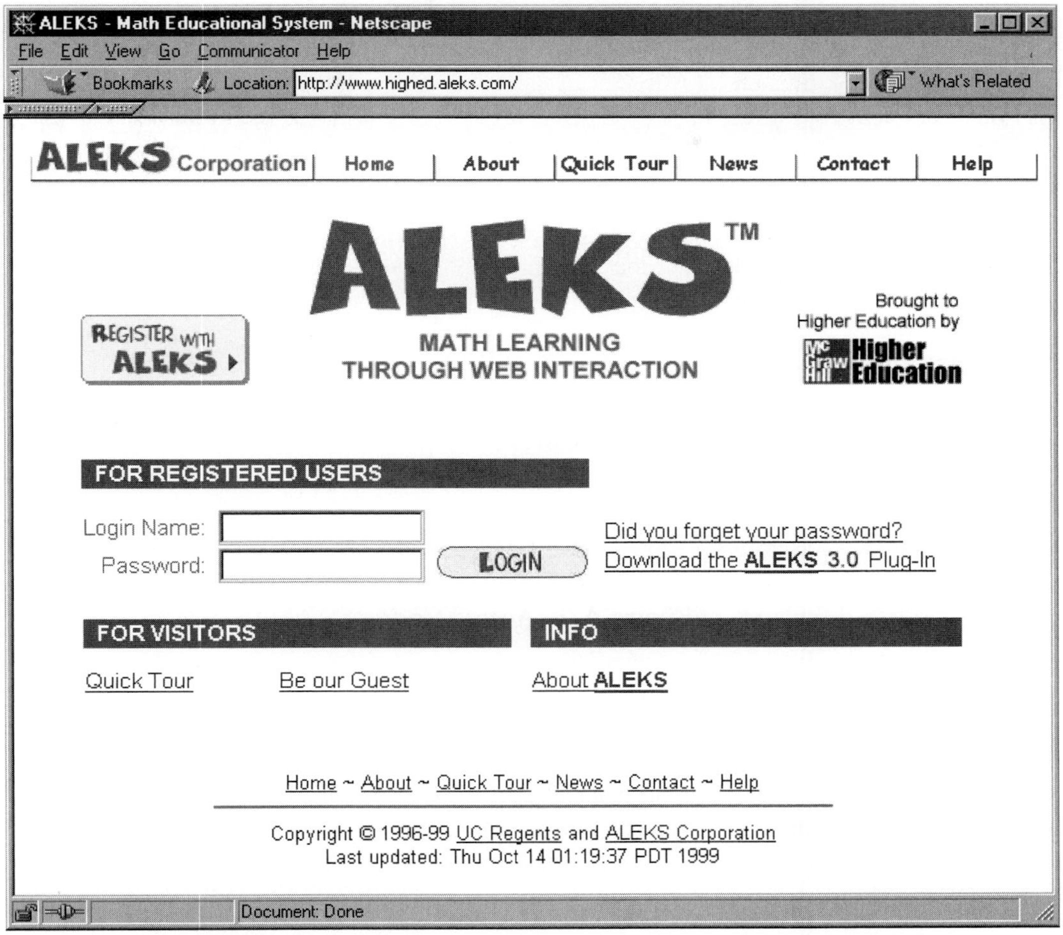

Figure A.1: The ALEKS Website for Higher Education

http://www.highed.aleks.com

NOTE: If you are typing this URL by hand, pay careful attention to the spelling "aleks." Also, the other **ALEKS** websites you might find using a search engine will not work for you. You will be able to register *only* at the address given above.

For your convenience, add a "Bookmark" or "Favorite" at this location. This is the site where you will log in to your account.

Step 2: Click on "Register with ALEKS" (Fig. A.1).

Step 3: You will see instructions for students and instructors registering with **ALEKS**. Click on "Register" where it says "For Students" (on the left-hand side).

NOTE: If you do not have a current plugin, one will be installed. Do not interrupt

Figure A.2: Access Code

this process until a message appears saying that the installation is complete. Then you will need to quit your Web browser ("Exit," "Close," or "Quit" under the "File" menu) and open your Web browser again. Then go back to the **ALEKS** website for Higher Education (use your Bookmark/Favorite). Return to Step 1, above, to begin registration.

Step 4: At the beginning of registration you will be asked for your **Access Code**. It is on a sticker inside the back cover of this booklet. Enter the Access Code in the spaces provided and click on "Next" (Fig. A.2). Answer the questions to complete your registration. Among other questions, you will be asked to enter your email address. Supplying this information enables your site administrator to help you with problems more quickly. You will also be asked to enter your Student ID number. Please double-check this number before clicking on "Next."

Step 5: At the end of registration you will be given a Login Name and Password. Write these down and keep them in a safe place. You will need them to return to the system (Sec. A.6). Your Login Name is not the same as your name. It usually consists of the first letter of your first name plus your whole last name run together, with no spaces or punctuation. Thus "Jane Smith" may have the Login Name "jsmith"; if there is more than one "Jane Smith" in the database, a numeral will be appended, as "jsmith2." You can change your Password at any time (Sec. A.5.5).

NOTE: Your Login Name and Password can be typed with upper- or lower-case letters. Neither may contain spaces or punctuation.

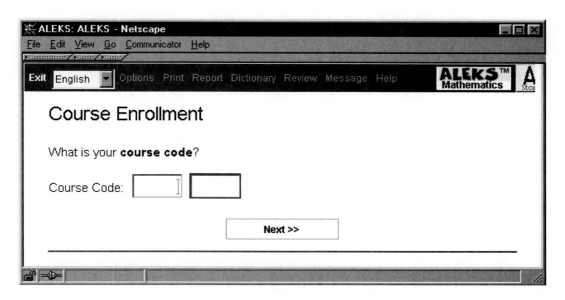

Figure A.3: Course Code

Step 6: Following registration you will be asked for your **Course Code**. The Course Code is supplied by your instructor. Enter this in the spaces provided and click on "Next" (Fig. A.3). Now you can begin the Tutorial.

A.4 Tutorial

The **ALEKS** system does not use multiple-choice questions. All answers are mathematical expressions and constructions. After registration, the **ALEKS** Tutorial will teach you to use the simple tools needed for your course (Fig. A.4). There is plenty of feedback to help you complete it successfully.

NOTE: The Tutorial is not intended to teach mathematics. It just trains you to use the **ALEKS** input tool (called the "Answer Editor"). The correct input is always shown, and you simply enter what you see. Online help is also available while you are using **ALEKS** by clicking the "Help" button (Sec. A.5.5).

A.5 Assessments and Learning

A.5.1 Assessments

Instruction through **ALEKS** is guided by precise understanding of your knowledge of the subject. This information is obtained by assessments in which the system asks you to solve a series of problems. (The system's estimate of your knowledge is

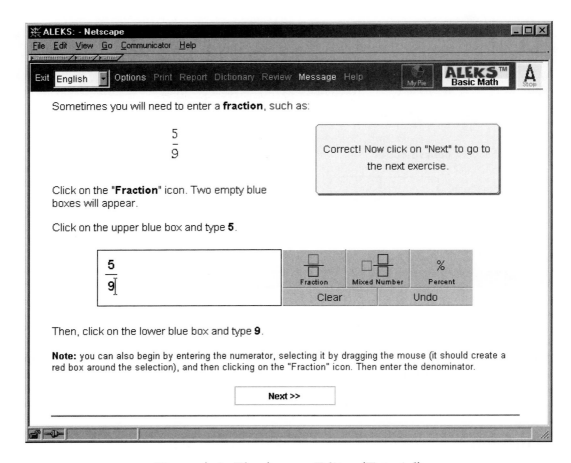

Figure A.4: The Answer Editor (Tutorial)

also updated when you make progress in the Learning Mode.) Your first assessment occurs immediately after the Registration and Tutorial. If you are enrolled in a course covering more than one subject you may go through multiple assessments. There will be one assessment for each subject.

NOTE: Your instructor may require that the first assessment be taken under supervision. **Don't try begin your initial assessment at home until you find out where your instructor wants you to take it.** Additional assessments may be scheduled for you by the instructor. These may or may not need to be supervised, depending on the instructor's preference. The **ALEKS** system also prompts "automatic" assessments when you have spent a certain amount of time on the system or have made a certain amount of progress.

Before the start of your first assessment you will be asked to estimate how well you know the subject. This information may make your assessment shorter, but it has no effect on the outcome or on the level where you will begin to use **ALEKS**. If you don't know, just select "Unknown."

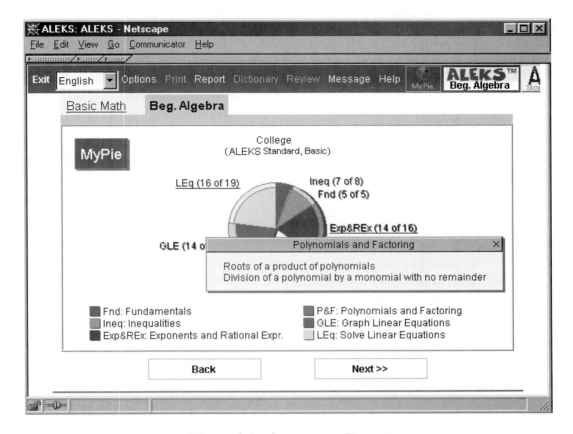

Figure A.5: Assessment Report

A.5.2 Results

Assessment results are presented in the form of color-coded piecharts. Slices of the piecharts correspond to parts of the syllabus. The relative size of the slices represents the importance of each topic for the syllabus. The solidly colored part of a slice indicates how close you are to mastering that part of the syllabus.

NOTE: You may see more than one piechart displayed following an assessment when you are progressing through a series of courses or units. (Your knowledge in the previous and/or subsequent units is also displayed.)

A.5.3 Learning Mode

Following the presentation of assessment results, the system will display a combined piechart ("MyPie"). This piechart shows the entire syllabus through the end of your current course. By placing the mouse pointer over slices of the pie, you can see which concepts you are now most ready to learn (Fig. A.5). Not all slices will contain concepts at any given time. They may have been mastered already, or work may need to be done in other slices before they become available. The concept you click on becomes your entry into the Learning Mode. The system will help you in seeking to master that concept and "add it to your pie."

A.5.4   Progress in the Learning Mode

In the Learning Mode, you are given practice problems based on the chosen topic. You also get explanations of how to solve this kind of problem and access to a dictionary of mathematical concepts. Underlined mathematical terms are links to the dictionary. Click on any term to get a complete definition. The system will require a number of correct answers before it assumes that you have mastered the concept. Then it "adds it to your pie." At this point a revised piechart will be shown reflecting your new knowledge. You will be able to choose a new concept to begin. If you make mistakes, more correct answers may be required. If you tire of this topic and wish to choose another, click on "MyPie" near the top of the window. This will make you exit the topic and you will get the piechart for a new choice. If you make repeated errors on a given concept, the system will conclude that the concept was not mastered. It will offer you a new choice of more basic concepts.

NOTE: Let **ALEKS** do its job! It is normal to have trouble mastering new concepts the first time around. When this happens, the system responds by revising its view of your knowledge and offers new choices. Keep in mind that the system does not "drill" you on concepts it believes you already know. The concepts presented as most "ready to learn" are always those just at the edge of your current knowledge. These are the topics you are completely prepared to learn.

A.5.5   Additional Features

All buttons described below are available in the Learning Mode. In the Assessment Mode, only the "Exit" and "Help" buttons are active.

Changing Your Password
If you want to change your Password, click on the "Options" button. Here you can also choose to look at your last Assessment Report and the work you've done recently in Learning Mode.

Report
Any time you wish to look at your assessment reports, click on "Report." Choose any date from the menu and click "Graph."

Dictionary
To search the online dictionary of mathematical terms, click "Dictionary."

Review
To review past material, click on the "Review" button. You will be offered a

choice of concepts to practice. An automatic review will also be prompted, if needed, when you log on.

Messages

Your instructor can send you messages via **ALEKS**. You see new messages when you log on. You can also check for messages by clicking on the "Message" button. Your instructor can choose to let you reply to messages as well.

Help

For online help with the use of the Answer Editor, click "Help."

MyPie

Clicking "MyPie" gives you a piechart summarizing your current mastery. You can use this piechart to choose a new concept.

A.6   Logging on to Your Account

Step 1: You always log on from the **ALEKS** website for Higher Education:

http://www.highed.aleks.com

Use the "Bookmark" or "Favorite" for this site if you made one (Sec. A.3). Remember that you may find other **ALEKS** websites via a search engine, but this is the only one with your account.

Step 2: On the login page enter the Login Name and Password provided at the time of registration (Sec. A.3, Step 5). Be sure to type these correctly, without any spaces or punctuation.

Step 3: If you enter your Login Name and Password correctly, your browser will begin accessing the plugin to start **ALEKS**. This takes a few seconds. You will then come to the place you left off in your previous **ALEKS** session.

NOTE: If you forget your Login Name or Password contact your instructor. It is a good idea to change your Password to one you will remember easily but is difficult for others to guess (Sec. A.5.5).

A.7   Installation on Additional Machines

Before You Begin: Installing **ALEKS** means installing the **ALEKS** plugin. This is the software used by your web browser to access and run **ALEKS**. You can access your **ALEKS** account from any computer that meets the technical requirements and has had the **ALEKS** plugin installed. You cannot use **ALEKS** without the **ALEKS** plugin that is installed over the World Wide Web.

Step 1: Go to the **ALEKS** website for Higher Education:

http://www.highed.aleks.com

Add a "Bookmark" or "Favorite" at this location.

Step 2: Use your Login Name and Password to log in (Sec. A.3, Step 5).

Step 3: When you log on to **ALEKS**, the system will automatically check to see if your system is compatible and if you have the most recent version of the **ALEKS** plugin. If you do not have a current plugin, it will download the plugin and ask your permission to install. After you grant permission, it will install the (new) plugin. Do not interrupt the installation process until a message appears stating that the installation is complete and asks you to restart your browser. You will need to quit your Web browser ("Exit," "Close," or "Quit" under the "File" menu), open your Web browser again, and go back to the **ALEKS** website for Higher Education (use your Bookmark/Favorite).

A.8   Guidelines for Effective Use

Supplementary Materials

You should have pencil and paper ready for all assessments and for use in the Learning Mode. Basic calculators should be used only when you are instructed to do so. (A basic calculator is part of **ALEKS**.)

Assessments

You should not ask for, nor receive any help during assessments. Not even explanations or rephrasing of problems are permitted. If you receive help, the system will get a wrong idea of what you are most ready to learn, and this will hold up your progress. Any time you are unsure of something, click "I don't know." (Don't guess!)

Learning Mode

You should learn to use the special features of the Learning Mode, especially the explanations and the mathematical dictionary. A button marked "Ask a Friend" may also appear from time to time. Clicking on this button will prompt the system to suggest the name of a classmate who has mastered the concept.

Regular Use

Nothing is more important to your progress than regular use of the system. Three hours per week is a recommended *minimum*. Five is better. Put **ALEKS** into your weekly schedule and stick to it!

A.9 Frequently Asked Questions

What are the rules for taking an assessment in ALEKS?

[**Sec. A.8**] You must have paper and pencil when taking an assessment in **ALEKS**. For Basic Math, no calculator is permitted. For Algebra, you should also have a simple calculator (no graphing or symbolic functions). A basic calculator is part of **ALEKS**. No help whatsoever is permitted, not even to the extent of rephrasing a problem. Cheating is not a danger, since students are given different problem-types in different sequences. Even if, by chance, two students sitting next to one another were to get the same problem-type at the same time, the actual problems would almost certainly have different numerical values and require different answers. During the assessment, you are not told if your answer is right or wrong. In the Learning Mode, however, you are always told if you make a mistake, and often what that mistake was. The assessment is not a test. Its main purpose is to determine what you are most ready to learn and help you make the best progress possible toward mastery.

How do I add concepts to my pie?

[**Sec. A.5.4**] You fill in your pie and achieve mastery in the subject matter by working in the Learning Mode on concepts and skills that the assessment has determined you are most "ready to learn." When you master a concept in the Learning Mode by successfully solving an appropriate number of problems, you will see that your piechart has been changed by the addition of that concept. The goal is to fill in the pie completely.

Why is it that I mastered all the concepts in the Learning Mode, but my assessment says I still have concepts to learn?

In the Learning Mode you are always working on one concept at a time, whereas assessments are cumulative and "test" you on everything in the given subject matter. It may be more difficult to show mastery of concepts you have recently worked on, when you are being quizzed on many different topics at the same time. For this reason, your assessment results may not exactly match what you had mastered in the Learning Mode. This is normal and simply means that you should keep working in the system. (Sometimes the opposite also occurs. That is, progress in the assessment turns out to be faster than in the Learning Mode.)

Why doesn't my piechart show any concepts from a category if I haven't filled in that category yet?

[**Sec. A.5.3**] You are completely "ready to learn" a set of concepts or skills when you have mastered all the prerequisite concepts or skills that they demand. To take an elementary example, in order to learn "addition of two-digit numbers with carry" you might have to first learn "addition of two-digit numbers without carry" and nothing else. Your piechart will not offer you concepts to work on if you are not ideally ready to begin learning them, that is, they have prerequisites you have not yet mastered. For this reason, your piechart may show that you have only mastered 8 out of 10 concepts for a particular slice of the pie (a particular part of the curriculum), but the piechart says you have no concepts available from that slice to work on. This means that the concepts you have left to master have prerequisites in other areas of the curriculum that you must master first. Keep working in the other slices, and eventually the concepts in that slice will become "available."

What is the difference between "Explain" and "Practice"?

When you begin working on a particular concept in the Learning Mode, you will be shown the name of the concept, a sample problem, and a choice between "Practice" and "Explain." If you think you know how to solve the problem, click "Practice." You will be given a chance to solve the same problem that was initially displayed. If you are not sure, click "Explain" to produce an explanation of how to solve the displayed sample problem. At the bottom of the Explanation page you have the "Practice" button, and sometimes other options for more detailed explanations and help. The Explanation page may also contain a link or reference to a McGraw-Hill textbook. If you click the "Practice" button following an explanation, you are offered a different problem of the same type, not the one whose solution was explained. In order to master the concept and add it to your pie, you must successfully solve a certain number of "Practice" problems. If you wish to choose a new concept, click the "MyPie" button on the **ALEKS** menu bar.

How does the Learning Mode help me learn?

[**Sec. A.5.4**] In the Learning Mode, do your best to solve the problems that are offered you. Do not lightly change topics or stop before the system tells you that you are done or suggests choosing another concept. Get to know the features of the Learning Mode, especially the explanations and the Dictionary. The Learning Mode will always tell you if your answer is correct or not. In many cases it will provide information on the kind of error you may have made. Pay attention to this feedback and be sure you understand it.

Keep in mind that **ALEKS** is always giving you material that, in its estimation, you are ideally ready to learn. It does not offer material you have already mastered, except in the Review mode. To go back to concepts you have already worked on, click the "Review" button on the **ALEKS** menu bar.

How does ALEKS create practice problems?

ALEKS creates both Assessment and Practice problems by means of computer algorithms, based on the definition of a particular concept or skill to be mastered. Thus, a particular concept or problem-type may serve as the basis for a very large number of specific problems, each with different numerical values and sometimes (as in the case of word problems) differing in other ways as well. With **ALEKS**, you cannot "learn the test" or "teach to the test."

What happens if I don't learn a concept (or get tired of working on a concept)?

[**Sec. A.5.4**] You must answer what the system judges to be an appropriate number of Practice problems correctly to add a concept to your pie. If you make mistakes, you must answer more. **ALEKS** will always tell you when you have mastered the concept. You cannot make this decision for yourself. If you wish to stop working on a concept and choose another one, you can click on "MyPie." Keep in mind, however, that when you come back to the former concept you will must start from the beginning with it. It is usually better to do your best to master the concept you are working on, unless the system tells you to switch. If you are clearly not making progress, **ALEKS** will suggest that you choose something else to work on.

Why is ALEKS giving me things we haven't done in the course or that are too hard?

[**Sec. A.5.4**] The most common reason that problems seem too difficult is that you received some help in the assessment, and **ALEKS** has an incorrect estimate of your actual knowledge. The problem, however, corrects itself as soon as you stop getting help. When you fail to master several concepts, **ALEKS** will quickly bring you back to a more comfortable place.

Remember that **ALEKS** is designed to give you material that you are ideally prepared to learn. It will not "drill" what has already been mastered, except in the sense that old knowledge is continually being exercised in the acquisition of new knowledge. **ALEKS** has no idea what you have done or are doing in class from one week to the next. In **ALEKS** you follow an individualized path through the curriculum that is produced by your own learning and your own choices.

Why is ALEKS giving me a new assessment?

[**Sec. A.5.1**] New assessments are automatically prompted by **ALEKS** when you have spent sufficient time in the Learning Mode or when you have made adequate progress. Your instructor may also request an assessment for you personally, or for everyone in the course. In this case it may be stipulated that the assessment must be taken in the computer lab. (If you attempt to work at home when an assessment has been ordered to be done in the lab, **ALEKS** will tell you that you need to log on from the lab and deny access.)

How can I get a new assessment in ALEKS?

You cannot initiate a new assessment. **ALEKS** or your instructor must make the request.

Why do I need to take a Tutorial to use ALEKS?

[**Sec. A.4**] The Tutorial is a brief interactive training program that teaches you to use the **ALEKS** input tools, or "Answer Editor." **ALEKS** does not use multiple-choice questions. Rather, it requires that answers be given in the form of mathematical expressions and geometrical and other constructions. The Answer Editor is a flexible set of tools enabling you to provide such answers. Although the Answer Editor is easy to use, the Tutorial will make sure you are completely proficient with it before beginning the **ALEKS** system. The Tutorial guides you through every step of learning to use the Answer Editor.

What can I do if I make a mistake entering an answer?

If you make an error entering an answer with the Answer Editor, click on "Undo" to go back one step, or on "Clear" to start over. You can also use the "Backspace" key on your keyboard in the usual way.

NOTE: You cannot use "Undo" or the "Back" button on your browser to go back if you have submitted an answer by clicking on "Next." If you realize that the answer you submitted was incorrect, don't be concerned; the system will most likely recognize this as a careless error based on your other answers and make allowances for it.

What are the icon buttons for?

The icon buttons are used to enter mathematical symbols and to create forms for mathematical expressions. In some cases the keyboard equivalents for icon buttons can be used.

Why are the buttons "sticky"?

[**Sec. A.10**] The buttons in the **ALEKS** interface may seem "sticky" at first. If so, try clicking them just a bit longer than usual. You will quickly get used to them.

Why doesn't anything appear when I type?

[**Sec. A.10**] In order to type input in the Answer Editor you must first click on a blue box. Each blue box in the input area corresponds to a mathematical expression. When you click on an icon button for a complex expression, it may place more than one blue box in the space, one for each part of the expression. Each blue box must be filled in for a complete expression. For instance, when you click on the "Exponent" icon button, you get two blue boxes. The big one is for entering the base, and a smaller one that is raised and to the right is used to enter the exponent.

How do I get help while using ALEKS?

[**Sec. A.5.5**] You can get help using the Answer Editor by clicking the "Help" button on the **ALEKS** menu bar.

Can my instructor or friend help me (or can I use a calculator) in the Learning Mode?

[**Sec. A.8**] Help and collaboration are allowed in the Learning Mode. Keep in mind, however, that if you get too much help, the system will start giving you problems that you are not prepared to solve. As a general rule, you can get help with one Practice problem, but you should solve the others yourself.

You need paper and pencil for the Learning Mode, just as you did for the assessment. Use of a calculator is permitted in Algebra only (without symbolic or graphing functions). A basic calculator is part of **ALEKS**.

Why are some of the words I see underlined?

[**Sec. A.5.5**] Underlined words in the Learning Mode are links to the online mathematics dictionary. Click on any underlined word to see its definition.

You can also access the Dictionary by clicking the "Dictionary" button on the **ALEKS** menu bar. The Dictionary is not available during assessment.

Note that the Dictionary is opened in a new window. When you are finished reading the definition, close or "Minimize" the window, and you will see the previous screen. Clicking "Back" on the browser won't work.

What is the "Ask a Friend" button for?

[**Sec. A.8**] The "Ask a Friend" button sometimes appears when you are having difficulty with a particular concept. When you click on the button, the system suggests the name of a classmate who has mastered the concept and may be able to help you.

How can I change my Password?

[**Sec. A.5.5**] You can change your Password by clicking the "Options" button on the **ALEKS** menu bar.

How can I review material I have already worked on?

[**Sec. A.5.5**] Click on the "Review" button to work on material you have already spent time on.

How can I see the reports from previous assessments?

[**Sec. A.5.5**] To see any of your assessment reports, click on "Report" (on the **ALEKS** menu bar).

How can I choose a new topic to work on?

[**Sec. A.5.5**] To see your current piechart and choose a new concept in the Learning Mode, click on "MyPie" (on the **ALEKS** menu bar), move around on the pie, and choose.

How can I print something in ALEKS?

[**Sec. A.10**] To print the contents of the screen, click "Print" on the **ALEKS** menu bar. This produces a new, printable window (**ALEKS** output is not normally printable). Depending on your browser, you may also have to click the browser's "Print" button. When you are done, close the new window.

What do I do if it's taking too long for a new page to load (or if the program freezes)?

[**Sec. A.10**] It shouldn't take more than a few seconds for **ALEKS** to respond when you click on any button. If you experience delay, freezing, or crashing, your first step is to click on the small "A" button at upper right. If this doesn't work, click your browser's "Reload" or "Refresh" button. If this doesn't work, close your browser and restart it. In extreme cases use Ctrl-Alt-Delete (Cmd-Opt-Esc on Macintosh). You will come back to the exact place you left off after you log back on.

How do I exit the ALEKS program?

To leave **ALEKS**, click the "Exit" button on the **ALEKS** menu bar or simply close your browser. **ALEKS** always remembers where you left off and brings you back to that place.

Why do I have to log on to ALEKS?

[**Sec. A.1**] The fact that **ALEKS** is used over the World Wide Web means that you can access it from your college computer lab or from home. As a registered user of **ALEKS**, you have an account on the server that contains a record of all the work you have done. Your instructor and administrators at your college have access to these records. They can monitor your progress and use of the system as well as carry out administrative functions. Web access also means that there is almost no maintenance or technical preparation required—no disks, CDs, peripherals, or backup procedures.

What if I have a question or problem using ALEKS?

If you have a question or problem using **ALEKS** that is not answered here, contact your instructor. Your instructor has been provided with extensive information on the operation of **ALEKS** and should be able to answer almost any question you may have.

What if I forget my Login Name or Password?

If you lose your Login Name or Password, contact your instructor.

A.10   Troubleshooting

Login Not Successful

First of all, be careful to type your Login Name and Password correctly, with no spaces or punctuation. Then, be sure you have accessed the **ALEKS** website for Higher Education. There is more than one **ALEKS** website, and only the one at which you registered contains your account. Use the URL provided in this booklet rather than looking for "aleks" via a search engine.

Sticky Buttons

Buttons in the **ALEKS** interface respond differently on different platforms. Sometimes you have to hold the mouse button down a bit longer than is usual. With some practice you should become accustomed to it.

Typed Input Does Not Appear

If you have trouble entering numbers or symbols in the Answer Editor, be sure that you have clicked on a blue box and that the pointer is within the answer area (the rectangle containing the blue boxes).

NOTE: It is not always possible to use the number keys on your keyboard's right-hand "keypad" (check that "Num Lock" has been pressed).

Mixed Number Difficulties

The Answer Editor is easy to use. One warning, however: mixed numbers must be entered using the Mixed Number icon, not by entering the whole part and then using the Fraction icon.

Freezing and Slow Response

If you are logged on to **ALEKS** and the program is either not responding or taking too long to load a new page, one of the following three actions may help (try them in the order given):

1. click on the small "A" in the upper right-hand corner of the **ALEKS** window;

2. click on your browser's "Reload" (or "Refresh") button;

3. close the browser and log on again (the system will bring you back to where you left off); if you cannot close the browser use Ctrl-Alt-Delete (PC) or Cmd-Opt-Esc (Macintosh) and end the task (or reboot, if all else fails).

Open applications other than the web browser that you are using to access **ALEKS** are another cause of slowness. Closing these applications may correct the problem.

If slowness persists, it is most likely due to a problem in the local network. Bring this to the attention of your system or lab administrator.

Lengthy Assessment

It is impossible to know how many questions will be asked in an assessment. The number of questions asked does not reflect your knowledge of the subject matter. It may reflect the consistency of your effort or concentration.

Reduction of Piechart

You may observe a loss of concepts in your piechart either in the Learning Mode or following an assessment. This is not a malfunction in the system, but results from errors made by you on material you had previously seemed to master. Don't worry: that is the way the system works. In particular, it is not unusual to have a "bad" assessment, one that, for external reasons (bad mood, distractions, etc.), does not reflect your actual knowledge. **ALEKS** will quickly bring you back to where you belong.

Problems Too Difficult

It is important to keep in mind that **ALEKS** will not offer concepts that it considers you already to have mastered. Rather, it presents material that you are currently most ready to learn. When the system gives problems that are too hard, the reason is often that you received help or guidance during the assessment or in the Learning Mode. This situation will soon correct itself if you have difficulty with the proposed concepts. The system will revise its estimate of your knowledge and offer concepts that you are more ready to learn.

Repeated Final Assessments

You may need to take more than one final assessment even after you have filled in your pie (in the Learning Mode). This is normal, since mastery is determined by the assessment, not by the Learning Mode. The system needs to confirm (in the assessment) that the entire curriculum has been mastered.

Printing Problems

To print **ALEKS** output (for instance, an Assessment Report) you must press the **ALEKS** "Print" button (on the **ALEKS** menu bar). This opens a new browser window containing the contents of the previous window in the form of a "Print Preview." When this page has been printed it should be closed to return to the normal **ALEKS** interface.

Index

NOTES

NOTES

NOTES